W9-BRY-858

KIM MARSHALL

ENGLISH
PART B

Math ENGLISH
VOCABULARY
VOCABULARY English READING
MATH MATH READING
ENGLISH Reading Vocabulary

Educators Publishing Service, Inc.
Cambridge and Toronto

Acknowledgments

Without the frank comments of my students in the sixth grade of the Martin Luther King School in Boston between 1970 and 1975, this book would not be what it is today. My students gave me new insights every day, and they deserve much credit for the sequencing, organization, and task analysis of the book. I would also like to thank my wife, Rhoda Schneider, for her unceasing and invaluable support over the last ten years.

Educators Publishing Service, Inc.
75 Moulton Street, Cambridge, Massachusetts 02238-9101

Contents

Vowels 1

Consonants 7

Prefixes 14

Suffixes 21

Alphabetical Order and Syllabication 28

Synonyms, Antonyms, and Homonyms 35

Common Homonyms 42

Rhyming 49

Nouns 56

Plurals of Nouns 63

Verbs 70

Past Tense of Verbs 77

Other Tenses 84

Pronouns 91

Adjectives 98

Adverbs 105

Articles and Prepositions 112

Conjunctions and Interjections 119

Sentence Patterns 126

All Parts of Speech 133

Final Review Test 138

To the Student

English is divided into *Part A* and *Part B* and includes a total of thirty-six units. These books are designed to improve your knowledge in English grammar, writing skills, and word analysis. If you work carefully through each unit, you should become a better writer and reader, and also you should know many of the words that teachers and writers use to talk about our language.

This is *English — Part B*, and it covers the following areas.
1. Word analysis — vowels and consonants, prefixes and suffixes, synonyms and antonyms (Units 17 to 24)
2. Parts of speech — nouns, verbs, pronouns, adjectives, adverbs, articles, prepositions, conjunctions, and interjections (Units 25 to 36)

You will also find that this book is a review of all the material you learned in *English — Part A.* That book covers the following areas.
1. Writing skills — sentences, paragraphs, and letters (Units 1 to 7)
2. Usage — capitals and punctuation (Units 8 to 16)

Each unit introduces one skill. The first four pages of the unit teach the new material, and the fifth page is a test to see how much you have learned. The unit ends with a review page of short practice questions on the skills learned in previous units. By the end of this book, you should know the material so well that you will be successful on the final test.

The two-part box at the top of each page is for your grade. The number filled in is the number of questions on the page; the empty part of the box is for you or your teacher to write in the number of questions you got right. At the back of your book is a progress chart on which to record your grades as you go through the book.

I hope you find the book interesting and helpful. Good luck!

KIM MARSHALL

Unit 17 — Vowels 1

Learn the different vowel sounds. *

ă — short *a*, as in *pack*
ā — long *a*, as in *take*

ĕ — short *e*, as in *bet*
ē — long *e*, as in *meat*

ĭ — short *i*, as in *hit*
ī — long *i*, as in *mile*

ŏ — short *o*, as in *pot*
ō — long *o*, as in *mole*

ŭ — short *u*, as in *nuts*
ū — long *u*, as in *mule*

After each word, write the vowel sound that it makes. Then write the sign for that vowel sound.

1. gun ŭ_____	14. hit _____	27. shelf _____
2. tone _____	15. hill _____	28. table _____
3. get _____	16. hike _____	29. cube _____
4. seal _____	17. lot _____	30. self _____
5. let _____	18. greet _____	31. candle _____
6. goal _____	19. take _____	32. wax _____
7. peel _____	20. shed _____	33. wake _____
8. guile _____	21. toll _____	34. chest _____
9. plate _____	22. green _____	35. temple _____
10. tag _____	23. little _____	36. six _____
11. leg _____	24. grip _____	37. seven _____
12. pad _____	25. gripe _____	38. peace _____
13. paid _____	26. quack _____	39. sense _____

*Note that diacritical markings may differ from one dictionary to another.

1

Put each word from the list below in the right group according to its vowel sound. Note that _y_ is sometimes used as a vowel and can say / ē / as in _sunny_ or say / ī / as in _dry_.

elf	act	odd	smile	sag	bone
wind<u>y</u>	melt	sly	joll<u>y</u>	meal	pig
dip	sail	mile	mod	ply	pale
sod	why	seal	gun	fun	Jude
ill	pile	felt	dope	mule	happ<u>y</u>
eel	up	dale	cute	moan	pal

1. Short _a_ sound, / ă /

_____

_____

_____

2. Long _a_ sound, / ā /

_____

_____

_____

3. Short _e_ sound, / ĕ /

_____

_____

_____

4. Long _e_ sound, / ē /

_____

_____

_____

5. Short _i_ sound, / ĭ /

_____

_____

_____

6. Long _i_ sound, / ī /

_____

_____

_____

7. Short _o_ sound, / ŏ /

_____

_____

_____

8. Long _o_ sound, / ō /

_____

_____

_____

9. Short _u_ sound, / ŭ /

_____

_____

_____

10. Long _u_ sound, / ū /

_____

_____

_____

11. _y_ as long _i_, / ī /

_____

_____

_____

12. _y_ as long _e_, / ė /

_____

_____

_____

Think up at least five words for each vowel sound. You can use the dictionary to find words if you want to.

1. short *a* sound, / ă /, as in *bag* _____

2. long *a* sound, / ā /, as in *take* _____

3. short *e* sound, / ĕ /, as in *leg* _____

4. long *e* sound, / ē /, as in *meal* _____

5. short *i* sound, / ĭ /, as in *hit* _____

6. long *i* sound, / ī /, as in *mile* _____

7. short *o* sound, / ŏ /, as in *got* _____

8. long *o* sound, / ō /, as in *mole* _____

9. short *u* sound, / ŭ /, as in *guts* _____

10. long *u* sound, / ū /, as in *mule* _____

Now write the vowel sound contained in each word below. Be careful — they're not what they look like!

1. steak _____ ā _____

2. en<u>ou</u>gh _____

3. great _____

4. sea _____

5. shield _____

6. rough _____

7. said _____

8. break _____

9. thief _____

10. myth _____

Here is a mixed-up list of 40 words. Sort them out into the different vowel sounds so that there are four in each one.

green	rub	flit	mule	happy	late
mile	cube	gun	oh	no	is
mole	shoal	jute	nail	slot	you
got	steam	style	had	sly	tried
myth	great	grief	rough	nest	rob
get	spat	enough	sin	an	
rat	said	freight	sled	lot	

1. Short *a* sound, / ă /

_____

_____

_____

_____

2. Long *a* sound, / ā /

_____

_____

_____

_____

3. Short *e* sound, / ĕ /

_____

_____

_____

_____

4. Long *e* sound, / ē /

_____

_____

_____

_____

5. Short *i* sound, / ĭ /

_____

_____

_____

_____

6. Long *i* sound, / ī /

_____

_____

_____

_____

7. Short *o* sound, / ŏ /

_____

_____

_____

_____

8. Long *o* sound, / ō /

_____

_____

_____

_____

9. Short *u* sound, / ŭ /

_____

_____

_____

_____

10. Long *u* sound, / ū /

_____

_____

_____

_____

Write five words for each vowel sound. You can spell the sound in different ways if you like (*steak* in the long *a* group, for example) as long as the vowel sound is right.

1. short *a* sound, / ă / _____

2. long *a* sound, / ā / _____

3. short *e* sound, / ĕ / _____

4. long *e* sound, / ē / _____

5. short *i* sound, / ĭ / _____

6. long *i* sound, / ī / _____

7. short *o* sound, / ŏ / _____

8. long *o* sound, / ō / _____

9. short *u* sound, / ŭ / _____

10. long *u* sound, / ū / _____

Now identify the vowel sound in the underlined letter or letters in each word.

1. funn<u>y</u> _____ē_____

2. n<u>ei</u>ghbor _____

3. m<u>y</u>th _____

4. l<u>ai</u>d _____

5. pl<u>y</u> _____

6. t<u>ou</u>gh _____

7. rel<u>ie</u>f _____

8. b<u>ea</u>t _____

Add one kind of punctuation (. ? ! "" ' , : ;) to each sentence below.

1. Why are you looking at me that way

2. Send me these things a book, a magazine, a pen, and some writing paper.

3. Where is the school? she asked. I can't find it in this big city.

4. This chicken is too well cooked

5. She left early in the morning but the snow made her late for work.

6. Come when you can we will hold dinner until you get here.

7. The boys mother was a good tennis player.

8. This isnt a joke, you know.

9. Go see what is the matter with the furnace

Capitalize the words that need it. There will be twenty capitals in all.

1. they spent the night at a holiday inn in reno, nevada.

2. let's see whether you and i can finish this job by friday.

3. the woman from france had difficulty making herself understood in new york.

4. the colorado river carved the grand canyon out of rock over millions of years.

5. she preferred *newsweek* to *time* magazine.

In the sentences below, underline the subject once and the predicate twice.

1. The president's silver and white jet landed at Andrews Air Force Base.

2. Her dog ate the entire steak, and the family had to go out for dinner.

Use apostrophes to show possession.

1. dog/Harry_____

2. strike/teachers_____

3. Cadillac/Doris_____

4. voice/singer_____

Make these words into contractions.

1. should have _____

2. can not _____

3. would not _____

4. let us _____

5. I will _____

6. we are _____

Write *fragment, slang, double negative,* or *run-on* after each group of words below.

1. The kangaroo, an animal with a very strong tail. _____

2. I'm not going nowhere with you. _____

3. That's a groovy song, man. _____

4. I'm coming I'm trying to find my purse. _____

6

Some consonants are confusing because they have different sounds in different places. Read these words and identify the sound of the underlined consonant in each word.

s can say / s / as in *say*; *s* can say / z / as in *does*.	*c* can say / s / as in *cigar*; *c* can say / k / as in *cape*.	*g* can say soft *g*, / j /, as in *gym*; *g* can say hard *g*, / g /, as in *girl*.
/ s / or / z / sound?	/ s / or / k / sound?	soft / j / or hard / g / sound?
1. ea<u>s</u>y ____	1. a<u>c</u>e ____	1. <u>g</u>eneral ____
2. <u>s</u>issy ____	2. <u>c</u>andle ____	2. <u>g</u>arden ____
3. le<u>ss</u> ____	3. <u>c</u>ell ____	3. <u>g</u>entle ____
4. ho<u>s</u>e ____	4. ra<u>c</u>e ____	4. <u>g</u>iant ____
5. loo<u>s</u>e ____	5. <u>c</u>all ____	5. <u>g</u>asoline ____
6. lo<u>s</u>e ____	6. <u>c</u>ancer ____	6. <u>g</u>enerous ____
7. <u>s</u>end ____	7. can<u>c</u>er ____	7. <u>g</u>uard ____
8. no<u>s</u>e ____	8. <u>c</u>able ____	8. <u>g</u>loves ____
9. ha<u>s</u> ____	9. <u>c</u>arpet ____	9. <u>g</u>uilty ____
10. goe<u>s</u> ____	10. <u>c</u>elebrate ____	10. <u>g</u>enius ____
11. <u>s</u>ell ____	11. <u>c</u>areful ____	11. <u>g</u>eography ____
12. mu<u>s</u>eum ____	12. <u>c</u>afeteria ____	12. geo<u>g</u>raphy ____
13. gue<u>ss</u> ____	13. <u>c</u>entury ____	13. <u>g</u>enial ____
14. me<u>ss</u> ____	14. <u>c</u>offee ____	14. <u>g</u>eneral ____
15. advi<u>s</u>e ____	15. <u>c</u>ollege ____	15. <u>g</u>uess ____
16. ma<u>s</u>ter ____	16. <u>c</u>ereal ____	16. <u>g</u>oofy ____

ch can say / ch / as in *chance*; *ch* can say / k / as in *chrome*.
Identify the sound of the underlined consonants in each word.

/ ch / or / k / sound?

1. <u>ch</u>eese ____	6. <u>ch</u>orus ____	11. <u>ch</u>ampion ____
2. <u>Ch</u>rist ____	7. <u>ch</u>aos ____	12. <u>ch</u>oosy ____
3. <u>ch</u>oose ____	8. <u>ch</u>um ____	13. <u>ch</u>itterlings ____
4. <u>ch</u>arm ____	9. <u>ch</u>aracter ____	14. <u>ch</u>imp ____
5. <u>ch</u>osen ____	10. <u>ch</u>oice ____	15. <u>ch</u>ump ____

Consonants 2

Write these words in groups of five according to the consonant sounds they make.

candle	chorus	chaos	less	settle	choose	cereal	gypsy
choose	cancer	chilly	hose	gasoline	gin	guard	guess
cylinder	silly	cap	geography	ace	cancer	guilty	advise
garden	general	character	call	cheap	children	careful	generous
Christmas	museum	century	chicken	sell	choir	goes	goofy

g says soft g / j /

1. _____
2. _____
3. _____
4. _____
5. _____

g

g says hard g / g /

1. _____
2. _____
3. _____
4. _____
5. _____

c says / s /

1. _____
2. _____
3. _____
4. _____
5. _____

c

c says / k /

1. _____
2. _____
3. _____
4. _____
5. _____

ch says / ch /

1. _____
2. _____
3. _____
4. _____
5. _____

ch

ch says / k /

1. _____
2. _____
3. _____
4. _____
5. _____

s says / s /

1. _____
2. _____
3. _____
4. _____
5. _____

s

s says / z /

1. _____
2. _____
3. _____
4. _____
5. _____

In each group, circle the *two* words that don't have the same consonant sound as the other words.

1. / s / as in *say*

sleepy
century
soap
sugar
sip
cyanide
cell
cancer
simple
cereal

2. / k / as in *chrome*

Christmas
choir
keep
cable
can't
cereal
chorus
Christ
chapter
kettle

3. / j / as in *generous*

goes
general
Japan
gypsy
girl
gentle
Jim
gymnasium
jittery
jutting

4. / ch / as in *champ*

choose
champion
chitterlings
chorus
chump
chaos
chase
cheap
cheat
chums

5. / g / as in *gutter*

guts
gentle
garage
gypsy
gone
got
guppy
garbage
guard
garden

6. / z / as in *easy*

mu<u>s</u>eum
lo<u>s</u>e
loo<u>s</u>e
choo<u>s</u>e
oo<u>z</u>e
new<u>s</u>
boo<u>z</u>e
po<u>s</u>e
di<u>s</u>tance
goe<u>s</u>

7. / sh / as in *shudder*

ship   sugar
sure   cyanide
simmer   shapes

8. / s / as in *person*

di<u>s</u>tance   goo<u>s</u>e
loo<u>s</u>e   doe<u>s</u>
no<u>s</u>e   gra<u>c</u>e

Put these words into groups of ten which make the same consonant sound.

shutter	gently	goose	shape	clown	cellar	choose	simple
con man	jam	kept	cell	ceiling	choke	Jerry	chives
jive	cancer	sure	children	guts	guard	Christian	Japanese
sugar	garbage	settle	chunky	got	century	sinful	shack
champion	celebrate	ginger	gone	juice	gypsy	good	chef
shady	cyclone	Jim	garden	sheep	ship	Christmas	chump
garage	chaos	chilly	gin	character	kettle	gutter	chimpanzee
center	chose	chorus	surely				

/ s / as in *sun*

1. _____
2. _____
3. _____
4. _____
5. _____
6. _____
7. _____
8. _____
9. _____
10. _____

/ k / as in *keen*

1. _____
2. _____
3. _____
4. _____
5. _____
6. _____
7. _____
8. _____
9. _____
10. _____

/ j / as in *judge*

1. _____
2. _____
3. _____
4. _____
5. _____
6. _____
7. _____
8. _____
9. _____
10. _____

/ ch / as in *chew*

1. _____
2. _____
3. _____
4. _____
5. _____
6. _____
7. _____
8. _____
9. _____
10. _____

/ g / as in *gun*

1. _____
2. _____
3. _____
4. _____
5. _____
6. _____
7. _____
8. _____
9. _____
10. _____

/ sh / as in *should*

1. _____
2. _____
3. _____
4. _____
5. _____
6. _____
7. _____
8. _____
9. _____
10. _____

In each group, circle the words that don't belong there because the underlined consonant sounds are different. There can be two or three in each group. There are twenty in all.

1. c̲enter	2. j̲uice	3. C̲hristmas	4. s̲heepish
c̲elebrate	g̲ently	c̲hampion	s̲ugar
s̲ettle	J̲im	c̲himpanzee	s̲imple
s̲ugar	g̲esture	c̲hilly	s̲hip
c̲yclone	g̲in	c̲horus	s̲ure
c̲ell	g̲uard	c̲hildren	c̲hef
c̲apture	J̲erry	c̲hitterlings	s̲hack
c̲eiling	j̲ive	c̲hives	s̲hapely
c̲ellar	g̲ive	c̲hoke	s̲hady
c̲ancer	j̲am	c̲hump	s̲ample
s̲inful	g̲uts	c̲heerful	s̲urely
c̲ity	j̲immy	c̲apital	s̲hatter

5. c̲on man	6. noti̲c̲e	7. g̲arage	8. mu̲s̲eum
k̲ettle	le̲ss̲on	g̲one	lo̲s̲e
c̲an't	can̲c̲el	g̲ently	cho̲s̲e
c̲hoose	me̲ss̲age	g̲uts	goe̲s̲
c̲haos	loo̲s̲e	g̲ypsy	new̲s̲
c̲horus	lo̲s̲e	g̲utter	toe̲s̲
c̲lown	si̲s̲ter	g̲arden	let̲s̲
k̲ept	di̲s̲tance	g̲arbage	can̲c̲er
c̲haracter	po̲s̲e	g̲otten	po̲s̲e
c̲hapter	can̲c̲er	g̲oodies	ho̲s̲e
c̲ap	noo̲s̲e	g̲eneral	no̲s̲e

11

Write one example of a word for each of the following vowel sounds.

1. / ă / _____   5. / ĭ / _____   8. / ō / _____

2. / ā / _____   6. / ī / _____   9. / ŭ / _____

3. / ĕ / _____   7. / ŏ / _____   10. / ū / _____

4. / ē / _____

Add one kind of punctuation (. ? ! "" ' , : ;) to each sentence below.

1. Were in this together.

2. That is Kathys dog.

3. Where is my father

4. Get lost, she shouted.

5. She moved south for two reasons to find an interesting job and to escape the cold weather of the North.

6. Some people love mushrooms other people hate them.

7. I'm not feeling well

8. Oh my goodness, she's back

9. Go find your scarf please.

10. Now he's here now he isn't.

Underline a subject once and a predicate twice.

1. She loved to sing, dance, eat rich food, and stay up late.

2. The fire engine arrived at the scene, but the house was engulfed in flames.

After each group of words write *fragment, slang, double negative, run-on, needs capitals,* or *O.K.*

1. This is my very favorite kind of ice cream. _____

2. He's handsome he's kind he's gentle he loves me. _____

3. I can't get neither kind in none of these stores. _____

4. will you listen to me, terry? _____

5. Listen, I don't dig that rap. _____

6. Standing in the late afternoon sunlight. _____

Use numbers to show the correct order for the parts of a business letter.

____ Closing   ____ Salutation   ____ Your Address   ____ Body of Letter

____ Signature   ____ Date   ____ Name and Address of Addressee

Put capitals in the right places.

1. her father fought in the korean war.

2. snoopy is a character in a comic strip called peanuts.

3. Francine asked, "were you born in February?"

(continued)

Review Test 18

After each sentence, add correct punctuation; then write *declarative, interrogative, imperative,* or *exclamatory.*

1. What is the meaning of this__ _____

2. Heavens, he's gone__ _____

3. Go find her__ _____

4. I'm pretty happy__ _____

Add apostrophes to show possession.

1. horse/girl_____

2. car/men_____

3. horses/girls_____

4. minibike/Charles_____

Write the two words that make up the following contractions.

1. let's _____

2. we're _____

3. they'll _____

4. I'm _____

Prefixes are small pieces of words that are often put *before* root words to change their meaning. For example, the prefix *sub*, meaning "under" is added to the root word *marine*, meaning "water" to form the new word *submarine.*

Here are 21 common prefixes and their meanings.

Prefix	Meaning	*Prefix*	Meaning	*Prefix*	Meaning
anti	against	*micro*	very small	*re*	again
bi	two	*mini*	small	*sub*	under
circum	around	*mis*	wrong	*super*	better than
dis	not	*non*	not	*trans*	across
ex	used to be	*post*	after	*tri*	three
in	not	*pre*	before	*un*	not
inter	between	*pro*	for	*uni*	one

Circle the prefix in each of the following words and write the meaning of the whole word on the line.

1. (un)happy __not happy_____
2. minibike _____
3. ex-husband _____
4. transatlantic _____
5. insensitive _____
6. dissatisfied _____
7. submarine _____
8. antifreeze _____
9. prowar _____
10. superman _____
11. unicycle _____
12. bicycle _____
13. tricycle _____
14. interplanetary _____
15. unnatural _____
16. ex-convict _____
17. misspell _____
18. retype _____
19. microskirt _____
20. prepaid _____

Prefixes 2

Learn the meanings of these prefixes.

Prefix	Meaning	Prefix	Meaning	Prefix	Meaning	Prefix	Meaning
anti	against	*inter*	between	*post*	after	*super*	better than
bi	two	*micro*	very small	*pre*	before	*trans*	across
circum	around	*mini*	small	*pro*	for	*tri*	three
dis	not	*mis*	wrong	*re*	again	*un*	not
ex	used to be	*non*	not	*sub*	under	*uni*	one
in	not						

Circle the prefix in each of the following words, and write the meaning of the whole word on the line.

1. (dis)contented _not contented_

2. supermarket _____

3. circumnavigate _____

4. transoceanic _____

5. triangle _____

6. antislavery _____

7. ex-wife _____

8. undignified _____

9. prewar _____

10. rewrite _____

11. nonsense _____

12. postgraduate _____

13. prebirth _____

14. unbearable _____

15. international _____

16. biannual _____

17. minibus _____

18. prehistoric _____

19. intolerant _____

20. replant _____

21. pro-Nixon _____

22. inflexible _____

23. unacceptable _____

24. pre-election _____

25. mistaught _____

15

Write the meanings of each of the following prefixes. Choose your answers from the list below.

Meanings: not, very small, before, wrong, against, again, under, not, across, not, between, used to be, two, for, three, after, small, not, around, one, better than

1. anti _____

2. bi _____

3. circum _____

4. dis _____

5. ex _____

6. in _____

7. inter _____

8. micro _____

9. mini _____

10. mis _____

11. non _____

12. post _____

13. pre _____

14. pro _____

15. re _____

16. sub _____

17. super _____

18. trans _____

19. tri _____

20. un _____

21. uni _____

Circle the prefix in each word below and write the meaning of the whole word on the line.

1. prejudge _____

2. replace _____

3. unofficial _____

4. supersonic (*sonic* means the "speed of sound") _____
_____

5. prenatal (*natal* means "birth") _____

6. transcontinental _____

7. postmortem (*mortem* means "death") _____
_____

8. trilingual (*lingual* means "language") _____
_____

9. intercity _____

10. misapply _____

11. subterranean (*terra* means "earth") _____
_____

12. misconduct _____

13. unfinished _____

14. bilingual _____

15. inaccurate _____

16. antischool _____

17. dishonest _____

18. unicycle _____

19. microskirt _____

20. superwoman _____

21. pre-Stone Age _____

22. disqualify _____

23. substandard _____

Prefixes 4

Write the following prefixes next to their meanings.

anti	micro	re
bi	mini	sub
circum	mis	super
dis	non	trans
ex	post	tri
in	pre	un
inter	pro	uni

1. very small _____

2. after _____

3. again _____

4. between _____

5. around _____

6. against _____

7. better than _____

8. one _____

9. two _____

10. three _____

11. not _____

12. used to be _____

13. for _____

14. wrong _____

15. small _____

16. not _____

17. under _____

18. across _____

19. not _____

20. before _____

21. not _____

Use the prefixes to write *one word* for each of these meanings. You have had all of them before!

1. not happy ___unhappy_____

2. before the war _____

3. after the war _____

4. against freezing _____

5. paid for before _____

6. better than man _____

7. not satisfied _____

8. across the Atlantic _____

9. three wheels (cycle) _____

10. one wheel _____

11. two wheels _____

12. used to be a convict _____

13. for Kennedy _____

14. to type again _____

15. to spell wrong _____

16. a very small skirt _____

17. between states _____

18. under water (marine) _____

19. not natural _____

20. to sail around (navigate) _____

21. three angles _____

22. against slavery _____

Write the meaning of each prefix below.

1. anti _____
2. bi _____
3. circum _____
4. dis _____
5. ex _____
6. in _____
7. inter _____
8. micro _____
9. mini _____
10. mis _____
11. non _____
12. uni _____
13. post _____
14. pre _____
15. pro _____
16. re _____
17. sub _____
18. super _____
19. trans _____
20. tri _____
21. un _____

Circle the prefix in each of the following words, and write the meaning of the whole word on each line.

1. rewrite _____
2. insane _____
3. interstate _____
4. bicycle _____
5. ex-soldier _____
6. redig _____
7. proteacher _____
8. anti-intellectual _____
9. distasteful _____
10. preschool _____
11. microbus _____
12. misspell _____

Write one word for each of the following meanings by connecting prefixes to root words.

1. across the Atlantic _____
2. better than man _____
3. used to be a convict _____
4. a very small skirt _____
5. paid for before _____
6. a small bike _____
7. not satisfied _____
8. three wheels (cycle) _____
9. taught wrong _____
10. to sail around (navigate) _____

In each group below, circle the *one* word that doesn't have the same consonant sound as the others.

1. cheap	2. cable	3. gypsy	4. sleep	5. garage	6. loose	7. shipping	8. sneeze
cheer	chorus	Japan	simple	gopher	lose	sugar	noose
chorus·	kipper	general	sugar	gym	hose	sure	loose
chump	cereal	guts	soap	got	chose	simple	goose

Write one example of a word for each of the following vowel sounds.

1. /ă/ _____   5. /ĭ/ _____   8. /ō/ _____

2. /ā/ _____   6. /ī/ _____   9. /ŭ/ _____

3. /ě/ _____   7. /ŏ/ _____   10. /ū/ _____

4. /ē/ _____

For each sentence below, supply the right punctuation (. ? ! " " ' , : ;).

1. Ye gods, it's her

2. Come here Kevin.

3. Why should I

4. She excelled in three subjects math, science, and art.

5. Can I go too? she asked.

6. Shouldnt you ask her father first?

7. It was the first robbery in twenty years

8. The girls mothers came along for the ride.

9. It's an important point please listen carefully.

10. Go west, young man

After each group of words write *fragment, slang, double negative, run-on, needs capitals,* or *O.K.*

1. That ain't sensible. _____

2. Coming at the end of the school year. _____

3. He's here he's finally here let's welcome him. _____

4. can you come over for dinner friday? _____

5. Don't you never check your work? _____

6. It simply isn't going to be possible. _____

Underline a subject once and a predicate twice.

1. She longed to see her father again, but his plane was delayed by fog.

Use numbers to show the correct order for the parts of a friendly letter.

____ Signature   ____ Salutation   ____ Your Address

____ Date   ____ Body of Letter   ____ Closing

(continued)

19

Review Test 19

List four proper nouns.

1. _____ 2. _____ 3. _____ 4. _____

After each sentence, add correct punctuation; then write *declarative, interrogative, imperative, exclamatory.*

1. Do your homework___ _____

2. Help, save me___ _____

3. Can you sing well___ _____

4. This work is easy___ _____

In the following sentence, put capitals in the right places.

1. their old pontiac broke down as they drove through the outskirts of kansas city.

2. her birthday was in january, on the same day as martin luther king's.

3. the christian religion began almost two thousand years ago in the middle east.

4. she said, "why can't you admit you're wrong for once?"

A suffix is a small piece of a word often added to the *end* of a root word to add to or change its meaning.

The suffix *-less* means "without";
so *-less* added to the root word *hope* is *hopeless* or "without hope."
The suffix *-ful* means "full of";
so *-ful* added to the root word *grace* is *graceful* or "full of grace."

Here are twenty-four common suffixes and their meanings:

Suffix	Meaning	Suffix	Meaning
-able	able	*-ist*	a person who . . .
-al	belonging to	*-ive*	a person or thing that is . . .
-ally	like, belonging to	*-less*	without
-ant	a person who is . . .	*-like*	resembling
-ate	to make . . .	*-ly*	like
-er	a person who . . .	*-ment*	the result of an action
-est	most	*-ness*	someone or something which has the quality of . . .
-ful	full of		
-fully	like someone or something full of	*-ous*	full of
-ic	like	*-some*	someone or something that tends to be . . .
-ing	a person or thing which		
-ish	like	*-tion*	the act of
-ism	state of being	*-y*	like

Circle the suffix in each word. Then write the root word on the line. If there is an * by the word, it means that the spelling of the root word will change. Be careful!

1. quick(ly) ___quick___

2. mov(able)* ___move___

3. doubtful_____

4. sinfully_____

5. blindness_____

6. agreement_____

7. argument*_____

8. bothersome_____

9. taxable_____

10. hopefully_____

11. bitterness_____

12. slowest_____

13. biggest*_____

14. respectful_____

15. sincerely_____

16. helpless_____

17. frantically_____

18. happiness*_____

19. finalist_____

20. regional_____

Now make new words by adding suffixes to the following root words; make as many as you can from each one. Use a dictionary to check your work if you need to.

1. quick_____

2. slow_____

3. like_____

4. govern_____

5. self_____

6. meet_____

7. help_____

8. respect_____

21

Remember these suffixes.

-ly	-ate	-ic	-ous	-like	-ment
-some	-ive	-y	-tious	-ish	-ist
-ism	-tive	-ant	-tion	-er	-ing
-al	-ful	-able	-ness	-est	-less
-ally	-fully				

Circle the suffix or suffixes in each word, and write the root word on the line. Be careful!

1. hatefully hate _____

2. helpful _____

3. terribly* _____

4. famous* _____

5. selfish _____

6. fearless _____

7. grateful _____

8. greatly _____

9. capitalism _____

10. lonesome _____

11. reasonable _____

12. government _____

13. likeness _____

14. fastest _____

15. courageous _____

16. nationally _____

17. personally _____

18. finalist _____

19. awfully* _____

20. momentous _____

21. operational* _____

22. printable _____

23. readable _____

24. immediately _____

In the word list below, find pairs of words that have the same root word. Write each pair on the lines, and then circle all the prefixes and suffixes in both words.

graceless	disagree	submarine	happiness	insincere	agreement
unhappy	ungraceful	sincerely	sensible	mariner	insensitive

1. graceless _____

2. ungraceful _____

1. _____

2. _____

1. _____

2. _____

1. _____

2. _____

1. _____

2. _____

1. _____

2. _____

Circle the suffix in each word below and then write the root word on the line. An * means you should be careful.

1. swinging_____
2. establishment_____
3. faster_____
4. lively_____
5. slowest_____
6. sickness_____
7. ignorant*_____
8. faithful_____
9. wonderfully_____
10. happiness*_____

11. massive_____
12. truly*_____
13. organism_____
14. noisily*_____
15. blindly_____
16. kisser_____
17. bigger*_____
18. bearable_____
19. scary*_____
20. childlike_____

On the lines put together the pairs of words in this list that have the same root word. Then circle all the prefixes and suffixes in both words.

unmatched	helpless	premature	disagree	marketable	involvement
unhelpful	supermarket	universal	successfully	versatility	agreement
unsuccessful	matchless	uninvolved	maturely		

1. unmatched _____
2. matchless _____

1. _____
2. _____

1. _____
2. _____

1. _____
2. _____

1. _____
2. _____

1. _____
2. _____

1. _____
2. _____

1. _____
2. _____

Suffixes 4

Circle the suffix in each word below, and then write the root word on the line. Some words are tricky, so be sure the root word looks right.

1. secretive _____
2. truly _____
3. truism _____
4. marketable _____
5. sincerity _____
6. believable _____
7. simplicity _____
8. greatness _____
9. helplessness _____
10. greeting _____

11. wasteful _____
12. sickness _____
13. smaller _____
14. rapidly _____
15. fatal _____
16. finally _____
17. productive _____
18. nursing _____
19. faithfully _____
20. jumpy _____

On the lines put together the pairs of words in this list that have the same root word. Then circle all the prefixes and suffixes in both words.

ingrate	grateful	lawless	ex-champion	championship	oceanographer
unlawful	untroubled	unromantic	transoceanic	troublesome	cyclist
romantically	tricycle	repaint	painter		

1. _____
2. _____

1. _____
2. _____

1. _____
2. _____

1. _____
2. _____

1. _____
2. _____

1. _____
2. _____

1. _____
2. _____

1. _____
2. _____

Circle the suffix in each word below and write the root word on the line.

1. gracefully _____
2. restless _____
3. quickest _____
4. piggish _____
5. scientist _____
6. sharper _____
7. interesting _____
8. happiness _____
9. lonesome _____

10. passionate _____
11. attractive _____
12. quietly _____
13. painfully _____
14. jumpy _____
15. taxable _____
16. selfish _____
17. government _____
18. famous _____

On the lines put together the pairs of words in this list that have the same root word. Circle all the prefixes and suffixes in both words.

disrespect	microscope	submarine	unicycle	unhopeful	mariner
unhappy	respectfully	telescopic	happiest	angular	cyclist
hopelessly	postrevolution	revolutionary	triangle		

1. _____
2. _____

1. _____
2. _____

1. _____
2. _____

1. _____
2. _____

1. _____
2. _____

1. _____
2. _____

1. _____
2. _____

1. _____
2. _____

Circle the prefix in the following words and write the full meaning on the line.

1. predawn _____
2. transatlantic _____
3. inhospitable _____
4. bicycle _____

5. miniskirt _____
6. dislike _____
7. unicycle _____
8. retype _____

Underline the subject once and the predicate twice.

1. Her cat and parakeets were killed in the fire, but her dog survived.

After each group of words, write *fragment, slang, double negative, run-on, needs capitals, needs punctuation,* or *O.K.*

1. I don't think he's never coming. _____
2. The king, riding on his beautiful black horse. _____
3. the charles river overflowed its banks after the storm. _____
4. Look out for that car _____
5. Like I don't catch your meaning. _____
6. The shortstop made a spectacular diving catch. _____
7. The car skidded the driver struggled to control it. _____

What happens to the first word in each paragraph? _____

What is the fourth thing you write in a business letter? _____

List four common nouns.

1. _____ 2. _____ 3. _____ 4. _____

In each sentence below, put capitals where they belong.

1. her father was english and her mother was russian, but she became an american.
2. passover is one of the most important religious holidays for jewish people.
3. his favorite cereal was cheerios, but his brother preferred frosted flakes.
4. she believed that god created the earth and would give her life after death.

Label the following sentence *declarative, interrogative, imperative,* or *exclamatory.*

1. What kind of sentence is this? _____

(continued)

Review Test 20

Put quotation marks in the right places in the sentences below.

1. If you listen carefully, said their teacher, you will get an A on the test.

2. He shouted through the bars, Give me my freedom! I demand to be released.

Use apostrophes to show possession.

1. cat/man _____   2. country/boys _____

Make these contractions.

1. It is _____   2. do not _____   3. will not _____

Put commas in the right places.

1. Come over here Arthur and I will show you something.

2. No I don't agree with you.

3. The ground was wet but they still had the game.

After each word, write the long or short vowel sound that it makes.

1. get __   2. shone __   3. hate __   4. mile __   5. scatter __   6. got __   7. mule __

Below are two groups of words for you to put in alphabetical order.
Remember: if the first letter is the same, look at the second letter. If that is the same, look at the third, and so on.

president   1. _____
under
odd   2. _____
dinner
dress   3. _____
add
immense   4. _____
depressed   5. _____
paste
yellow   6. _____

7. _____

8. _____

9. _____

10. _____

senior   1. _____
signal
salvage   2. _____
sinner
sullen   3. _____
sudden
silly   4. _____
summer   5. _____
sense
simple   6. _____

7. _____

8. _____

9. _____

10. _____

Now break the following words into syllables. Say the word to yourself and make sure you break it into the right number of pieces.
Remember: a one-syllable word cannot be broken up. If you're not sure how to do this, look up the word in the dictionary.

1. summer <u>sum-mer</u>

2. yesterday _____

3. green _____

4. sinner _____

5. single _____

6. bracelet _____

7. banjo _____

8. colder _____

9. spring _____

10. singer _____

11. window _____

12. telephone _____

13. lightning _____

14. attention _____

15. winter _____

16. floorboards _____

Below are two groups of words for you to put in alphabetical order.
Remember: if the first letter is the same, look at the second letter, then the third, and so on.

nice	1. _____	strong	1. _____
great		song	
fantastic	2. _____	silver	2. _____
super		seem	
lovely	3. _____	seam	3. _____
tremendous	4. _____	strap	4. _____
wonderful		strip	
magnificent	5. _____	string	5. _____
glorious	6. _____	sad	6. _____
exciting		supper	
	7. _____		7. _____
	8. _____		8. _____
	9. _____		9. _____
	10. _____		10. _____

Break the following words into syllables. Say the word to yourself and make sure you break it into the right number of pieces.
Remember: a one-syllable word cannot be broken up. Use a dictionary if necessary.

1. moment _____   10. movement _____

2. thirteen _____   11. silent _____

3. schoolboy _____   12. effort _____

4. hunter _____   13. city _____

5. painter _____   14. table _____

6. problem _____   15. direction _____

7. probation _____   16. concentrate _____

8. actor _____   17. typewriter _____

9. automobile _____   18. monster _____

Alphabetical Order and Syllabication 3

Put the following states in alphabetical order.

Maryland
Virginia
California
Arkansas
Georgia
Wyoming
Utah
Colorado
Ohio
Idaho
Michigan
Montana
Massachusetts
Florida
Maine
New Hampshire
Vermont
Connecticut
West Virginia
Nevada
Oregon
Texas
Oklahoma
Kansas
Missouri

Break the following words into syllables.
Remember: a one-syllable word cannot be broken up.

1. famous _____
2. midnight _____
3. bullet _____
4. laughing _____
5. center _____
6. bicycle _____
7. filthy _____
8. knife _____
9. punish _____
10. punishment _____
11. tackle _____
12. knowledge _____
13. silver _____
14. pencil _____
15. admire _____
16. captain _____
17. rocket _____
18. bookshelf _____
19. toaster _____
20. college _____
21. bandage _____

Put the following countries in alphabetical order.

Greece
England
New Zealand
Mauritania
Australia
Brazil
Scotland
Nigeria
Spain
Portugal
Honduras
Panama
Argentina
Germany
Russia
South Korea
North Korea
South Africa
Egypt
Liberia
Chad
Upper Volta
Mongolia
Mexico
Canada

Break the following words into syllables.

1. September _____

2. wonderful _____

3. prefix _____

4. postpone _____

5. beautiful _____

6. fishy _____

7. hundred _____

8. underneath _____

9. America _____

10. pillow _____

11. pillbox _____

12. artist _____

13. heater _____

14. radiator _____

15. teacher _____

16. leaderless _____

17. ceiling _____

18. concise _____

19. purple _____

20. yellow _____

21. boiling _____

Put the following cities in alphabetical order.

Washington	Albuquerque	Hollywood
New York	Wabash	Providence
Denver	San Francisco	Great Falls
Boston	Newark	Peoria
Chicago	Los Angeles	Sioux City
Wilmington	Cincinnati	Dallas
Brewster	Kansas City	Worcester
Atlanta	Beverly Hills	Seattle
Portland		

_____

_____

_____

_____

_____

_____

_____

_____

_____

_____

_____

_____

_____

_____

_____

_____

_____

_____

_____

_____

Break the following words into syllables.

1. mousetrap _____

2. summertime _____

3. breakfast _____

4. telephone _____

5. pillowcase _____

6. signal _____

7. bookshelf _____

8. speaker _____

9. English _____

10. picture _____

11. November _____

12. seventeen _____

13. hundred _____

14. paper _____

15. Negro _____

16. urbanite _____

17. seventy _____

18. champion _____

19. slavery _____

20. children _____

21. celebration _____

In the following words, circle the prefixes and suffixes and underline the roots.

1. hopeful   3. taxable   5. unhappiness   7. pretrial

2. unlikely   4. interstate   6. hateful   8. finalist

Circle the prefixes and then write the full meaning of the following words.

1. misspell _____   4. superman _____

2. triangle _____   5. submarine _____

3. ex-wife _____   6. postgame _____

In each group circle the word with a different consonant sound.

1. chump	2. lose	3. simple	4. chorus	5. surely	6. garage	7. kept	8. general
chip	loose	sure	character	soap	gypsy	cannot	garden
chaos	hose	sugar	cheer	Sicily	general	center	gentle

After each word, write the long or short vowel sound that it makes.

1. kept __   3. real __   5. scatter __   7. gutter __   9. sub __

2. post __   4. mule __   6. soap __   8. sit __

Put one kind of punctuation in each sentence below and write what the punctuation is called on the line to the right.
These are your choices:

| period (.) | exclamation mark (!) | colon (:) | quotation marks (" ") |
| comma (,) | question mark (?) | semicolon (;) | apostrophe (') |

1. I don't like the look of this Susan._____

2. At last, here he is_____

3. She paused and said, That music is the most lovely I've ever heard._____

4. The boys fathers all came to the cookout._____

5. When will that plane arrive_____

6. Fetch these things a pencil, a ruler, and some crayons._____

7. Dont you want to put on some gloves?_____

8. I'm sure the criminal will be caught_____

9. The play went on for hours finally it ended._____

10. Go see what's in the refrigerator_____

Label the following sentence _declarative_, _interrogative_, _imperative_, or _exclamatory_.

1. Please find the missing words. _____

(continued)

33

Review Test 21

Name five places where you need to use capitals.

1. _____   3. _____   5. _____

2. _____   4. _____

List four common nouns.

1. _____   2. _____   3. _____   4. _____

What is the fifth part of a friendly letter? _____

Label the following groups of words *fragment, slang, double negative, run-on,* or *O.K.*

1. The truck won't never get here. _____

2. Doing what comes naturally. _____

3. This sentence is all right. _____

4. We gotta find a better way. _____

5. It seems right I think you have the answer. _____

Unit 22—Synonyms, Antonyms, and Homonyms 1

Remember:
   synonyms mean almost the same thing.
   antonyms mean opposite things.
   homonyms sound the same.

Write *synonyms, antonyms,* or *homonyms* after each pair below.

1. here and hear _____
2. sad and happy _____
3. nice and good _____
4. hare and hair _____
5. threw and through _____
6. glad and happy _____
7. day and night _____
8. naked and clothed _____
9. bear and bare _____
10. learning and education _____

11. clean and dirty _____
12. nice and mean _____
13. nice and kind _____
14. beach and beech _____
15. two and too _____
16. night and knight _____
17. cool and warm _____
18. boy and girl _____
19. boiling and hot _____
20. rough and smooth _____

Now think of synonyms for the words below.

1. hunt _____
2. very cold _____
3. friend _____
4. shine _____

Think of antonyms for the words below.

1. soft _____
2. slim _____
3. war _____
4. fast _____
5. smart _____
6. evil _____

Synonyms, Antonyms, and Homonyms 2

Remember:
>   *synonyms* mean almost the same thing.
>   *antonyms* mean opposite things.
>   *homonyms* sound the same.

Write *synonyms*, *antonyms*, or *homonyms* after each pair below.

1. excellent and terrible _____

2. simple and easy _____

3. site and sight _____

4. huge and enormous _____

5. man and woman _____

6. devil and God _____

7. find and lose _____

8. win and lose _____

9. find and discover _____

10. lady and woman _____

11. due and do _____

12. sleepy and wide-awake _____

13. insane and crazy _____

14. sharp and dull _____

15. sandy and rocky _____

16. right and write _____

17. through and threw _____

18. near and faraway _____

19. buy and by _____

20. kill and murder _____

Give synonyms for the words below. Use slang if you want to.

1. money _____

2. help _____

3. road _____

4. drugs _____

5. cute _____

6. happy _____

7. odd _____

8. hot _____

Give antonyms for the words below.

1. heartbroken _____

2. heaven _____

3. roof _____

4. palace _____

5. ceiling _____

6. light _____

Synonyms, Antonyms, and Homonyms 3

Define:

1. synonyms _____

2. antonyms _____

3. homonyms _____

Use the words below to fill in the blanks.

cold	well-known	road	insane	due	soft
zero	courageous	low	so	far	two
haul	dear	threw	mail	weak	murder
beautiful	right	sour	unhappy	automobile	by
rush	late	enormous	sell	dirty	yew

Synonyms

1. famous _____

2. sad _____

3. kill _____

4. hurry _____

5. brave _____

6. nothing _____

7. street _____

8. crazy _____

9. huge _____

10. car _____

Antonyms

1. hot _____

2. sweet _____

3. strong _____

4. near _____

5. ugly _____

6. high _____

7. hard _____

8. buy _____

9. early _____

10. clean _____

Homonyms

1. too _____

2. through _____

3. sew _____

4. dew _____

5. buy _____

6. write _____

7. male _____

8. hall _____

9. deer _____

10. you _____

Write *synonyms, antonyms,* or *homonyms* after each pair below.

1. walk and run are _____

2. their and they're are _____

3. low and high are _____

4. teacher and instructor are _____

5. ugly and unattractive are _____

6. rude and polite are _____

37

Define:

1. synonyms _____

2. antonyms _____

3. homonyms _____

Use the words below to fill in the blanks.

soft	run	their	conceal	hell	hair
jail	truthful	won't	impolite	right	ill
beach	yes	lies	where	pig	freezing
ate	full	amusing	fair	hear	not
silent	dwarf	weight	female	bale	filthy

Synonyms

1. hide _____

2. honest _____

3. hog _____

4. funny _____

5. quiet _____

6. sick _____

7. prison _____

8. midget _____

9. dirty _____

10. rude _____

Antonyms

1. hard _____

2. will _____

3. no _____

4. boiling _____

5. empty _____

6. male _____

7. walk _____

8. heaven _____

9. left _____

10. truth _____

Homonyms

1. there _____

2. wear _____

3. fare _____

4. wait _____

5. eight _____

6. beech _____

7. hare _____

8. here _____

9. bail _____

10. knot _____

Write *synonyms, antonyms,* or *homonyms* after each pair below.

1. ceiling and floor are _____

2. mountain and valley are _____

3. no and know are _____

4. knowledge and ignorance are _____

5. friendly and companionable are _____

6. town and village are _____

7. write and type are _____

Define:

1. synonyms _____

2. antonyms _____

3. homonyms _____

Write _synonyms, antonyms,_ or _homonyms_ after each pair below.

1. sad and happy are _____

2. close and near are _____

3. bee and be are _____

4. hero and coward are _____

5. their and they're are _____

6. loose and tight are _____

7. lose and find are _____

8. rare and common are _____

9. easy and simple are _____

10. sew and so are _____

Use the words below to fill in the blanks.

rested	fresh	big	two	lies
crazy	ate	dear	night	enemy
threw	learning	wet	kind	kill

Synonyms

1. large _____

2. nice _____

3. education _____

4. murder _____

5. insane _____

Antonyms

1. truth _____

2. dry _____

3. friend _____

4. tired _____

5. rotten _____

Homonyms

1. too _____

2. through _____

3. deer _____

4. eight _____

5. knight _____

Use a diagonal line to break the following words into syllables. Use a dictionary if necessary.

1. country

2. mandolin

3. sinister

4. expedition

5. typist

6. housesitter

7. paper

8. lightning

Underline a subject once and a predicate twice.

1. The sheriff in the big black hat arrested the criminal.

2. The wind howled through the trees, and three birches blew down.

Label the following groups of words *fragment, slang, double negative, run-on, needs capitals, needs punctuation,* **or** *O.K.*

1. The rope snapped twenty kids tumbled down everyone laughed. _____

2. Why don't you ask someone else that question _____

3. He's handsome, and that ain't a lie. _____

4. The man who loved to dance the tango. _____

5. She set a blistering pace in the first mile of the marathon. _____

6. There wasn't nothing left to do. _____

7. her childhood sweetheart moved to arizona. _____

Use numbers to show the correct order for the following parts of a business letter.

____ Date   ____ Signature   ____ Body of Letter   ____ Closing

____ Salutation   ____ Your Address   ____ Name and Address of Addressee

Capitalize the proper nouns below.

1. mexican   2. chair   3. restaurant   4. wheaties   5. hindu   6. correction

Label the following sentence *declarative, interrogative, imperative,* **or** *exclamatory.*

1. Good grief, it's crashing! _____

Put quotation marks in the following sentences. One doesn't need any.

1. Okay, said the coach, we can win or lose the game in the next five minutes.

2. The radio announcer said that there would be five feet of snow.

3. Her father ordered, Take out the garbage. Wash the dishes. Practice the piano.

Use apostrophes to show possession.

1. windows/building _____

2. food/cats _____

3. dictionary/Charles _____

4. party/children _____

(continued)

Review Test 22

Make the following words into contractions.

1. will not _____   2. there is _____   3. I will _____

Use numbers to show the alphabetical order of the following words.

____ string   ____ strike   ____ stipend   ____ stroke   ____ sop   ____ sample   ____ strum

Circle the prefixes and write the full meaning of the following words.

1. pregame _____   4. antiwar _____

2. prolife _____   5. misuse _____

3. circumnavigate _____

In the following words, circle the suffixes.

1. fitfully   2. establishment   3. lifelike   4. incidentally   5. exciting

Use a comma, colon, or semicolon in each sentence below.

1. There's no time to lose get your jacket.

2. Henry I love you.

3. Remember this you have five minutes left before the end of the test.

Fill in the blanks with the right words.
Remember these homonyms:

    to   He went *to* the market *to* buy bread.
    two   I would like *two* sandwiches.
    too   He wanted to go *too*. There were *too* many people.

1. "There is _____ much noise in here," said the teacher.

2. This is question number _____ .

3. He asked _____ use the car.

4. She walked _____ school with her little brother.

5. He was _____ young to see the movie.

6. The room was crowded with _____ many people.

7. She asked _____ talk to the principal.

8. They were _____ poor to buy a decent meal.

9. Most people have _____ eyes _____ see with.

10. He was _____ fat _____ fit through the narrow doorway.

11. May I come along _____?

Fill in the blanks with the right words.
Remember these homonyms:

    there   Look over *there*. *There* is no milk left.
    their   The students lost *their* books.
    they're (contraction of *they are*) *They're* feeling sick.

1. That is _____ house on the corner.

2. If you look over _____ you will see a new Cadillac.

3. _____ not going to be able to come to school today.

4. _____ is not enough room for both cars in the garage.

5. _____ clothes are always new and tasteful.

6. _____ is that boy who beat me up yesterday.

7. I rang the doorbell to see if _____ was any answer.

8. _____ house burned down yesterday; _____ going to have to stay with us.

9. _____ isn't going to be a big celebration for his birthday.

10. _____ going to show us _____ pictures if _____ is time.

11. I don't think _____ is any reason to argue about it.

12. They walked over to _____ grandmother's house.

Common Homonyms 2

Use each word below in a short sentence.

1. to _____

2. two _____

3. too _____

4. there _____

5. their _____

6. they're _____

Fill in the blanks with the right words.
Remember these homonyms:

    threw   He *threw* the baseball to second base.
    through The ball went *through* the window.

1. The policeman stopped them as they drove _____ the town.

2. He _____ the rock across the street.

3. She looked _____ the window at the street below.

4. Superman is supposed to be able to look _____ solid objects.

5. The Roman soldier _____ his spear at the enemy general.

Fill in the blanks with the right words.
Remember these homonyms:

    wear   She wanted to *wear* her new dress.
    where *Where* is that pencil?

1. Do you know _____ that bicycle is?

2. I don't want to _____ those pants because they are dirty.

3. _____ is the bathroom, please?

4. _____ do you think you're going?

5. Do you know _____ I can find something to _____ to that party?

Fill in the blanks with the right words.
Remember these homonyms:

    right   He raised his *right* hand. That is the *right* answer.
    write She started to *write* the letter.

1. Can you _____ your name upside down?

2. Take a _____ turn at the bottom of the hill.

3. Please _____ the _____ answer on the paper.

Use each word below in a short sentence.

1. to _____

2. two _____

3. too _____

4. there _____

5. their _____

6. they're _____

7. threw _____

8. through _____

9. wear _____

10. where _____

11. right _____

12. write _____

Fill in the blanks with the right words.

Remember these homonyms:

no   There is *no* milk left.

know Do you *know* the capital of Massachusetts?

1. Do you _____ how to get to Chicago from here?

2. The answer to that question is _____.

3. There is _____ way I am going to give you any money.

4. I don't _____ anyone who is as smart as you are.

Fill in the blanks with the right words.

Remember these homonyms:

fair   It's not *fair* that he can go and I can't.

fare   The *fare* on the bus is twenty-five cents.

1. If you can't pay the _____, you'd better get off.

2. The plane _____ to New York was $56.32.

3. She didn't think it was _____ that she got left behind.

4. I think it is only _____ that you should get some presents too.

5. He didn't think it was _____ for children to pay the full

_____ on the bus.

Use each word below in a short sentence.

1. to _____

2. two _____

3. too _____

4. there _____

5. their _____

6. they're _____

7. threw _____

8. through _____

9. wear _____

10. where _____

11. right _____

12. write _____

13. no _____

14. know _____

15. fair _____

16. fare _____

Fill in the blanks with the right words.
Remember these homonyms:
  cents She only had fifty *cents* left.
  sense Don't you have any *sense?*

1. The boy found seventy-five _____ on the ground.

2. She told him to use his common _____ in making the decision.

3. If you had any _____ , you would lend me ten _____ to get you a cone.

Fill in the blanks with the right words.
Remember these homonyms:
  hole They dug a *hole* in the ground.
  whole I can't believe I ate the *whole* thing!

1. Look out! There is a _____ in the road up ahead.

2. They painted that _____ room in just five hours.

3. The dentist filled up the _____ _____ with silver.

Use each word below in a sentence.

1. to _____

2. two _____

3. too _____

4. there _____

5. their _____

6. they're _____

7. threw _____

8. through _____

9. wear _____

10. where _____

11. right _____

12. write _____

13. no _____

14. know _____

15. fair _____

16. fare _____

17. cents _____

18. sense _____

19. hole _____

20. whole _____

Label the following pairs of words *synonyms,* *antonyms,* **or** *homonyms.*

1. write/right _____
2. straight/crooked _____
3. give/receive _____
4. cruel/mean _____
5. climb/mount _____
6. one/won _____

Use a diagonal line to break the following words into syllables.

1. workbook
2. lightly
3. unhappy
4. napkin
5. lastingly
6. entertainer
7. lawmakers
8. nibble
9. nightmarish
10. interfere

Number in alphabetical order.

____ break   ____ beak   ____ breech   ____ bucket   ____ back   ____ bread   ____ broken

Circle prefixes and suffixes.

1. tricycle   2. sincerely   3. ungraceful   4. insensitive   5. submariner

Circle the prefixes and then write the full meaning of the following words.

1. nonsense _____
2. antislavery _____
3. inflexible _____
4. replant _____
5. mistaught _____
6. intolerant _____

Circle the word that doesn't have the same consonant sound as the others in each group below.

1. gavel   gutter   gin
2. come   cereal   center
3. sure   sin   sugar
4. church   chapter   character
5. lo<u>s</u>er   no<u>s</u>e   hand<u>s</u>ome
6. cho<u>s</u>e   loo<u>s</u>e   noo<u>s</u>e
7. jingle   guard   gypsy
8. centipede   can   cup

After each word, write the long or short vowel sound that it makes.

1. cr<u>u</u>tch __   2. cr<u>u</u>el __   3. l<u>e</u>tter __   4. n<u>a</u>pe __   5. pr<u>a</u>ttle __   6. gu<u>i</u>le __   7. t<u>i</u>le __   8. t<u>i</u>tter __

Put one kind of punctuation in each sentence below, and write the name of the punctuation on the line to the right.
These are your choices:

period (.)   exclamation mark (!)   colon (:)   quotation marks (" ")
comma (,)   question mark (?)   semicolon (;)   apostrophe (')

1. Can you wait for another hour _____

2. I dont think its right that theyre late. _____

3. Look out behind you _____

4. Glorias mother got a new job. _____

5. Watch out for these things snakes, lions, and tigers. _____

6. He didn't think the world was going to end soon _____

(continued)

47

7. Go find some firewood _____

8. Not guilty, said the foreman of the jury.

   Free at last! said the defendant. _____

9. There was a long pause then the audience began to cheer. _____

10. As for you Arthur I am proud to give you first prize. _____

This is a declarative sentence. True or false? _____

Put capitals where they are needed.

1. She said, "this is the worst meal I've had in my life."

2. The note began, "dear john, i have to leave you for my boyfriend in california."

What is the sixth part of a business letter? _____

What happens to the first word in every paragraph? _____

Underline a subject once and a predicate twice.

1. The horse bucked wildly, but the cowboy managed to stay aboard.

Unit 24 — Rhyming 1

Let's face it: English is a crazy language. You can make the same vowel sound in many different ways. You just have to learn and remember the words that act strangely!

Use the lines below to put these words into groups of five that rhyme with each other. The first group has been done for you.

sun	suit	pole	low	me	sea	gun
fruit	den	son	lose	go	sole	shoes
goal	foe	free	shun	soul	fun	fen
gee	no	loot	mole	flea	choose	toot
snooze	news	sew	shoot	again	pen	when

1. sun 1. ___ 1. ___ 1. ___
2. son 2. ___ 2. ___ 2. ___
3. shun 3. ___ 3. ___ 3. ___
4. fun 4. ___ 4. ___ 4. ___
5. gun 5. ___ 5. ___ 5. ___

1. ___ 1. ___ 1. ___
2. ___ 2. ___ 2. ___
3. ___ 3. ___ 3. ___
4. ___ 4. ___ 4. ___
5. ___ 5. ___ 5. ___

In each group circle the word that *doesn't* rhyme with the others. The first two have been done for you.

1. cost	3. both	5. home	7. another	9. maid	11. wood
lost	cloth	come	brother	laid	good
(most)	moth	dome	bother	paid	food
	sloth	Rome	mother	said	hood

2.(give)	4. rough	6. beneath	8. knead	10. put	12. call
jive	tough	wreath	bead	but	hall
dive	enough	death	lead	rut	tall
alive	though	heath	head	jut	shall
arrive		sheath		cut	fall

49

Use the lines below to put these words into groups of five that rhyme with each other.
Remember: they don't have to be spelled exactly the same way; they just have to *sound* alike.

they're	know	leak	stayed	fare
Sue	take	though	mate	should
close	flew	seek	freight	fair
sew	would	steak	ghost	dew
grew	freak	nose	knows	throws
speak	grow	paid	due	make
post	made	stood	owes	delayed
break	eight	good	meek	date
most	there	crate	pear	roast
wood	so	toast	lake	laid

1. _____   1. _____   1. _____   1. _____

2. _____   2. _____   2. _____   2. _____

3. _____   3. _____   3. _____   3. _____

4. _____   4. _____   4. _____   4. _____

5. _____   5. _____   5. _____   5. _____

1. _____   1. _____   1. _____   1. _____

2. _____   2. _____   2. _____   2. _____

3. _____   3. _____   3. _____   3. _____

4. _____   4. _____   4. _____   4. _____

5. _____   5. _____   5. _____   5. _____

1. _____   1. _____

2. _____   2. _____

3. _____   3. _____

4. _____   4. _____

5. _____   5. _____

Use the lines below to put these words into groups of five that rhyme with each other.
Be careful!

supreme	beef	create	Morse	dam	jam
die	coast	laid	opaque	most	sing
horse	seem	sly	cue	gleam	mate
break	fade	slam	door	ring	oar
course	flue	bait	belief	force	lake
suede	hoarse	spring	eight	ache	aide
chief	clam	afraid	post	straight	my
bore	fling	grief	view	buy	for
host	toast	beam	I	theme	Pam
Jew	knew	steak	pour	leaf	bring

1. _____   1. _____   1. _____   1. _____

2. _____   2. _____   2. _____   2. _____

3. _____   3. _____   3. _____   3. _____

4. _____   4. _____   4. _____   4. _____

5. _____   5. _____   5. _____   5. _____

1. _____   1. _____   1. _____   1. _____

2. _____   2. _____   2. _____   2. _____

3. _____   3. _____   3. _____   3. _____

4. _____   4. _____   4. _____   4. _____

5. _____   5. _____   5. _____   5. _____

1. _____   1. _____   1. _____   1. _____

2. _____   2. _____   2. _____   2. _____

3. _____   3. _____   3. _____   3. _____

4. _____   4. _____   4. _____   4. _____

5. _____   5. _____   5. _____   5. _____

Use the lines below to put these words into groups of five that rhyme with each other.

so	thumb	owes	opaque	come	goes
aisle	throws	gloom	mile	loot	fake
grows	repair	lake	canoe	goal	parachute
ache	news	through	search	perch	church
do	though	swear	roll	shampoo	dumb
fruit	whom	drum	tow	Joe	millionaire
lurch	use	bare	take	exhume	Suze
tomb	chute	some	two	isle	nose
grow	smile	heir	loom	route	ooze
pole	besmirch	lose	control	bowl	style

1. _____   1. _____   1. _____   1. _____

2. _____   2. _____   2. _____   2. _____

3. _____   3. _____   3. _____   3. _____

4. _____   4. _____   4. _____   4. _____

5. _____   5. _____   5. _____   5. _____

1. _____   1. _____   1. _____   1. _____

2. _____   2. _____   2. _____   2. _____

3. _____   3. _____   3. _____   3. _____

4. _____   4. _____   4. _____   4. _____

5. _____   5. _____   5. _____   5. _____

1. _____   1. _____   1. _____   1. _____

2. _____   2. _____   2. _____   2. _____

3. _____   3. _____   3. _____   3. _____

4. _____   4. _____   4. _____   4. _____

5. _____   5. _____   5. _____   5. _____

Use the lines below to put these words into groups of five that rhyme with each other.

so	do	throws	though	isle	Joe
aisle	lake	use	take	fake	goes
grows	through	canoe	lose	owes	Suze
ache	news	opaque	two	shampoo	nose
smile	grow	mile	tow	style	ooze

1. _____   1. _____   1. _____   1. _____

2. _____   2. _____   2. _____   2. _____

3. _____   3. _____   3. _____   3. _____

4. _____   4. _____   4. _____   4. _____

5. _____   5. _____   5. _____   5. _____

1. _____   1. _____

2. _____   2. _____

3. _____   3. _____

4. _____   4. _____

5. _____   5. _____

Circle the correct homonyms in the sentences below.

1. We had lunch over at (there / their / they're) house.

2. Her little sister was just (to / two / too) slow on a bike.

3. The new jet streaked (threw / through) the clouds.

4. "You don't have the (right / write) to say that!" shouted the man.

5. I (no / know) what you want, and the answer is (no / know).

Label each group of words *fragment, slang, double negative, run-on, needs capitals, needs punctuation,* **or** *O.K.*

1. I don't think neither of them has the answer. _____

2. She stood up very straight as she gave the speech. _____

3. Ain't it ever going to quit raining? _____

4. I'm lonely I'm tired I need some rest. _____

5. Bending over looking for her lost contact lens. _____

6. Now listen Harvey I don't want to ask you again. _____

7. The result of the race was a dead heat. _____

Underline a subject once and a predicate twice.

1. She was born in Mexico City, but she and her family moved to Texas in 1962.

What is the second part of a friendly letter? _____

Capitalize the proper nouns.

1. garage   2. country   3. holiday inn   4. jew   5. cincinnati   6. friday

Label the following sentence *declarative, interrogative, imperative,* **or** *exclamatory.*

1. Go to the store. _____

Put one kind of punctuation in each sentence below, and write the name of the punctuation on the line to the right.
These are your choices:

| period (.) | exclamation mark (!) | colon (:) | quotation marks (" ") |
| comma (,) | question mark (?) | semicolon (;) | apostrophe (') |

1. Why can't you admit you're wrong _____

2. This is it, he said. It's now or never. Jump! _____

3. They found Georges father in the supermarket. _____

4. The bricks of the old house were crumbling _____

(continued)

5. I'm alive, you maniac _____

6. These are your chores clean the sink, wash the floor, and rake leaves. _____

7. Yes I am the one who put it there. _____

8. Go see what you can find _____

9. Were going to have to take another route. _____

10. Now it's over we can go home. _____

After each word, write the long or short vowel sound that it makes.

1. Yule __   3. hut __   5. shot __   7. clone __   9. spite __

2. Chevrolet __   4. slay __   6. gem __   8. pit __   10. sass __

Write *synonyms* or *antonyms* after the following pairs of words.

1. living/dying _____   2. ridiculous/silly _____

Use numbers to show alphabetical order.

____ cryptic   ____ crystal   ____ cross   ____ critic   ____ caller   ____ cyst   ____ crisis

Circle the prefixes and then write the full meanings to the following words.

1. mistype _____

2. transcontinental _____

3. interstate _____

Nouns are *people, places,* or *things.*

Write some nouns on the lines below.

People

1. _____
2. _____
3. _____
4. _____
5. _____

Places

1. _____
2. _____
3. _____
4. _____
5. _____

Things

1. _____
2. _____
3. _____
4. _____
5. _____

Now circle the nouns in the following sentences. The number in parenthesis at the end tells how many nouns the sentence has in it.

1. There was a large black cat running across the floor. (2)

2. Her knees were sore from crawling across the desert. (2)

3. They used the new scissors to cut through the ribbon. (2)

4. The house burned down before the firefighters arrived. (2)

5. The movie appeared on television at 8:30 P.M. (2)

6. The police stopped the man in his car on the highway. (4)

7. The little boy was kidnapped near his home after school. (3)

8. The typewriter was broken so she had to handwrite the letter. (2)

9. The bomber swooped out of the clouds and dropped its load on the town. (4)

10. The knife wasn't sharp enough to cut through that steak. (2)

11. The dog attacked the mail carrier and tore her clothes. (3)

12. The boxer knocked out his opponent in the third round. (3)

13. Joseph and Edwin had a long chess game. (3)

14. Sal had a dream that Rich was chased by Frankenstein. (4)

15. Stacey couldn't find the key to her house anywhere. (3)

16. The man had an idea for a new invention. (3)

Nouns 2

Nouns are *people, places,* or *things.*

Circle the nouns in each sentence. The number in parenthesis at the end tells how many nouns the sentence has in it.

1. From Boston the jet flew to New York. (3)

2. Her brother won the marathon in Massachusetts. (3)

3. The gorilla pounded his hairy chest and ran off into the jungle. (3)

4. The house caught on fire because of some oily rags in the attic. (4)

5. My sister thought the paper was hidden somewhere in the closet. (3)

6. Her grandmother lived for many years after her own children died. (3)

7. The president flew around the country in his own special jet. (3)

8. A noun is a person, place, or thing. (4)

9. Henry Aaron holds the record for the most home runs in baseball. (4)

10. The hunter missed the duck and threw down his shotgun in disgust. (4)

11. The principal had a good idea. (2)

12. George showed the scary picture to his mother. (3)

13. Atlanta is the capital city of the state of Georgia. (4)

14. His favorite meats were veal, pork, bacon, and steak. (5)

15. The game lasted for a good seven hours before people finally left. (3)

16. The ambulance arrived just in time to save his life. (3)

17. The soldier stole the helicopter and landed by the White House. (3)

18. The bulb burned out after only a few days. (2)

19. Her favorite subject was spelling. (2)

20. The boy worked out the answer on his electronic calculator. (3)

Now write some sentences of your own.

1. Write one with one noun.

   _____

2. Write one with three nouns.

   _____

3. Write one with two nouns.

   _____

What is a noun? _____

Circle the nouns in the following sentences. The number in parenthesis at the end tells you how many nouns the sentence has in it. Make sure not to circle pronouns (words like *he, she, it, they*).

1. Where is that stupid pencil? (1)

2. The movie was very exciting—it was all about soldiers in the war. (3)

3. Her birthday was on Wednesday, but she didn't tell people about it. (3)

4. His grandmother died suddenly and he went to the funeral. (2)

5. She was taken to the hospital to have an X-ray. (2)

6. The woman tied a new yellow ribbon in her hair. (3)

7. The war in Vietnam lasted longer than any war in our history. (4)

8. Baseball can be a very boring sport. (2)

9. The dream was about her father returning with a big present for her. (3)

10. The new pen ran out of ink and was useless to her. (2)

11. The newspaper had a story about the fire on their street. (4)

12. Her answers were very neatly written, but the teacher marked them wrong. (2)

13. Her mother couldn't find that word in the dictionary. (3)

14. The vulture circled in the air over the body of the dying donkey. (4)

15. The clock was wrong, so she missed the appointment. (2)

16. The dentist seemed to enjoy drilling teeth and putting in fillings. (3)

17. She crumpled up the paper and threw it onto the floor. (2)

18. The horse can run faster over a long distance than any animal, even the cheetah. (4)

19. Two astronauts from the United States walked on the surface of the moon. (4)

20. The Sears Tower in Chicago is now the tallest building in the world. (4)

Now write some sentences of your own.

1. Write a sentence with four nouns.

_____

2. Write a sentence with one noun.

_____

What is a noun? _____

Think up your own nouns to fill in the lines in the following sentences.

1. He didn't see the _____ in time to stop.

2. The _____ walked toward her with a menacing expression.

3. He cut himself with a(n) _____ .

4. It didn't take them long to find the _____ .

5. A(n) _____ was all we needed to leave for the trip.

6. She drank a nice cool glass of _____ after the race.

7. There was too much _____ for them to see properly.

8. The enormous _____ towered over their heads.

9. The beautiful brown _____ rushed towards the open gate.

10. The _____ crashed and immediately started to burn.

Now do you know what a noun is? Circle all the nouns in the following sentences.

1. The new restaurant served really delicious spaghetti.

2. Her uncle gave her a camera for Christmas.

3. Her new watch was smashed in the accident.

4. That is the best idea you have had in three years!

5. The boat was hit by an enemy torpedo, and it sank to the bottom of the ocean.

6. Completely exhausted, their father left his job.

7. The rocket was launched from its silo underground in North Dakota.

8. The driver screeched to a halt and ran after the boys.

9. The report card was covered with good grades.

10. The grass was too long for them to see the snake.

Circle the nouns in the following sentences.

1. The ruler broke when the boy stepped on it.

2. They drove to Florida for a vacation in the sun.

3. The floor was covered with dirt and papers.

4. Her hair was a beautiful color.

5. The windows on the new building started to break when there was a strong wind.

6. The sky was filled with threatening clouds.

7. You could see his lips moving when he read a book.

8. The old pine tree was struck by lightning.

9. The grey horse was limping badly at the end of the race.

10. He had a dream that he was elected president.

11. The woman's cat got into a fight with five dogs.

12. It took her just ten minutes to put the puzzle together.

Now make a list of twenty nouns that you see, feel, or think about in your room.

1. _____
2. _____
3. _____
4. _____
5. _____
6. _____
7. _____
8. _____
9. _____
10. _____

11. _____
12. _____
13. _____
14. _____
15. _____
16. _____
17. _____
18. _____
19. _____
20. _____

Circle the word in each group that doesn't rhyme with the others.

1. live	2. though	3. come	4. bother	5. maid	6. wood	7. moth	8. most	9. death	10. put
give	tough	home	brother	paid	food	cloth	host	breath	but
dive	rough	some	mother	said	good	both	cost	wreath	jut

Circle the word in each group that doesn't have the same consonant sound as the others.

1. cellar	2. generate	3. gutter	4. choice	5. character	6. loose	7. sneeze	8. caller
celery	guard	gap	chorus	choose	nose	hose	cantilever
can't	generous	gypsum	chaos	chapter	noose	moose	celebrate

Circle the correct homonyms.

1. (There / their / they're) not very interested in dating.

2. The (to / two / too) of them had (to / two / too) much to eat and went (to / two / too) bed.

Label the following pairs of words *synonyms* or *antonyms*.

1. gargantuan / huge _____   2. philanthropic / miserly _____

Use diagonal lines to divide the following words into syllables.

1. freedom   2. cabbage   3. cavernous   4. lumberyard   5. kleptomaniac

Use numbers to show alphabetical order.

_____ gentry   _____ generous   _____ guppy   _____ grapple   _____ gone   _____ gripping   _____ go

For each word below, circle the prefix and write the word's complete meaning on the line.

1. misapply _____   4. intercity _____

2. prebirth _____   5. rewrite _____

3. unfinished _____   6. substandard _____

After each word, write the long or short vowel sound that it makes.

1. kidding __   2. gravy __   3. gravel __   4. gunner __   5. slot __   6. both __   7. kept __   8. keep __

Put one kind of punctuation in each sentence below, and write the name of the punctuation on the line to the right.
These are your choices:

| period (.) | exclamation mark (!) | colon (:) | quotation marks (" ") |
| comma (,) | question mark (?) | semicolon (;) | apostrophe (') |

1. The box contained the following tools a hammer, a saw, and a drill. _____

2. The wolf howled all night and in the morning the men saw it. _____

3. I'm not kidding you can go look for yourself. _____

(continued)

61

4. He released his grip and said, Now will you tell me where it is? Will you?_____

5. "Can I get an Amen" bellowed the preacher._____

6. Katys mother got a job as managing editor of the newspaper._____

7. This is going to be the last game_____

8. Lets see who can turn in the neatest paper._____

9. Look out, look out, look out_____

10. Find that missing marble_____

What is the first part of a business letter? _____

What is the point of dividing a story into paragraphs?_____

Correct the double negatives by rewriting the sentences below.

1. I don't never want any. _____

_____

2. I can't get neither one right. _____

_____

Write four proper nouns.

1. _____   2. _____   3. _____   4. _____

Below are seven rules for you to follow for making the plurals (more than one) of nouns. Try to learn the rules.

For most words just add s.

1. garden ___gardens___
2. hen _____
3. skyscraper _____
4. singer _____
5. table _____
6. typewriter _____
7. house _____
8. car _____

For words ending in y, change the y to i and add es.

1. city ___cities___
2. country _____
3. party _____
4. lady _____
5. navy _____
6. candy _____

But for words ending in ey, just add s.

1. valley ___valleys___
2. jockey _____
3. monkey _____

For words ending in f, change the f to v and add es.

1. leaf ___leaves___
2. shelf _____
3. half _____
4. calf _____

Some are just crazy, and you have to remember the plurals for each of them.

1. man ___men___
2. woman _____
3. child _____
4. tooth _____
5. goose _____
6. mouse _____
7. foot _____
8. deer _____
9. sheep _____
10. ox _____

For words ending in fe, change the f to v and add s.

1. knife ___knives___
2. wife _____
3. life _____

For words ending in o, ss, sh, ch, and x, add es.

1. tomato ___tomatoes___
2. pass _____
3. wish _____
4. church _____
5. fox _____
6. potato _____
7. dish _____
8. tax _____
9. mass _____
10. latch _____

Plurals of Nouns 2

Remember the rules:

   For most words, add *s*.
   For words ending in *y*, change the *y* to *i* and add *es*.
   But for words ending in *ey*, just add *s*.
   For words ending in *f*, change the *f* to *v* and add *es*.
   For words ending in *fe*, change the *f* to *v* and add *s*.
   For words ending in *o*, *ss*, *sh*, *ch*, and *x* add *es*.
   And for some crazy words you just must remember the plurals.

Write the plural of each noun below. Each group follows the same rule.

1. knife_____
2. life_____
3. wife_____

4. city_____
5. belly_____
6. penny_____
7. jelly_____
8. navy_____
9. candy_____

10. ruler_____
11. pen_____
12. light_____
13. house_____
14. plane_____
15. cloud_____
16. dream_____
17. clock_____
18. pencil_____

19. potato_____
20. Negro_____
21. mess_____
22. dress_____
23. fuss_____
24. lash_____
25. dash_____
26. latch_____
27. church_____
28. beach_____
29. box_____
30. tax_____
31. mix_____
32. hex_____

33. leaf_____
34. shelf_____
35. calf_____
36. half_____

37. man_____
38. woman_____
39. child_____
40. tooth_____
41. goose_____
42. mouse_____
43. foot_____
44. deer_____
45. sheep_____
46. ox_____

47. chimney_____
48. valley_____
49. monkey_____
50. jockey_____

Use the following rules to write the plural of each noun below.
    For most words, add *s.*
    For words ending in *y*, change the *y* to *i* and add *es.*
    But for words ending in *ey*, just add *s.*
    For words ending in *f*, change the *f* to *v* and add *es.*
    For words ending in *fe*, change the *f* to *v* and add *s.*
    For words ending in *o, ss, sh, ch,* and *x*, add *es.*
    And for some crazy words you just must remember the plurals.

1. man _____	22. copy _____
2. boy _____	23. class _____
3. potato _____	24. dish _____
4. dish _____	25. leaf _____
5. knife _____	26. belly _____
6. city _____	27. pass _____
7. mouse _____	28. teacher _____
8. chimney _____	29. hobby _____
9. woman _____	30. key _____
10. mass _____	31. Negro _____
11. shoe _____	32. peanut _____
12. child _____	33. wife _____
13. fox _____	34. wharf _____
14. goose _____	35. table _____
15. valley _____	36. army _____
16. church _____	37. taxi _____
17. tooth _____	38. sky _____
18. story _____	39. life _____
19. box _____	40. shelf _____
20. fly _____	41. deer _____
21. pie _____	42. monkey _____

Write the plurals of each of the following nouns. Remember the rules for forming plurals.

1. knife _____

2. wheel _____

3. dress _____

4. tooth _____

5. deer _____

6. mess _____

7. navy _____

8. life _____

9. jelly _____

10. floor _____

11. fuss _____

12. mix _____

13. goose _____

14. chimney _____

15. box _____

16. dictionary _____

17. monster _____

18. tomato _____

19. dash _____

20. wife _____

21. leaf _____

22. monkey _____

23. child _____

24. Negro _____

25. beach _____

26. penny _____

27. fight _____

28. lash _____

29. calf _____

30. ox _____

31. church _____

32. belly _____

33. plant _____

34. city _____

35. shelf _____

36. speech _____

37. valley _____

38. mouse _____

39. woman _____

40. catch _____

41. man _____

42. dance _____

43. brace _____

44. jockey _____

45. tax _____

46. sheep _____

47. half _____

48. machine _____

49. wharf _____

50. foot _____

Test 26 — Plurals of Nouns

Write the plurals of each of the following nouns. Remember the rules for forming plurals.

1. foot _____

2. wharf _____

3. machine _____

4. half _____

5. sheep _____

6. tax _____

7. jockey _____

8. mouse _____

9. dance _____

10. man _____

11. catch _____

12. woman _____

13. spring _____

14. valley _____

15. beach _____

16. shelf _____

17. city _____

18. plant _____

19. belly _____

20. church _____

21. ox _____

22. calf _____

23. lash _____

24. fight _____

25. penny _____

26. knife _____

27. tree _____

28. dress _____

29. tooth _____

30. deer _____

31. mess _____

32. navy _____

33. life _____

34. jelly _____

35. floor _____

36. fuss _____

37. mix _____

38. goose _____

39. chimney _____

40. box _____

41. dictionary _____

42. monster _____

43. tomato _____

44. dash _____

45. daisy _____

46. wife _____

47. leaf _____

48. monkey _____

49. child _____

50. Negro _____

Circle the following nouns.

1. funny   3. grow   5. country   7. president

2. slightly   4. dinner   6. through

Write four common nouns.

1. _____   2. _____   3. _____   4. _____

Underline the subject once and the predicate twice.

1. She doesn't see what I'm trying to say, and I am getting angry.

2. The long, drawn-out, boring, irritating conversation finally ended.

Write _fragment, slang, double negative, run-on, needs capitals, needs punctuation,_ or _O.K._ after each group of words below.

1. He wasn't nowhere in sight. _____

2. Quit horsing around, will you? _____

3. she didn't think i was serious. _____

4. The spaghetti wasnt cooked well enough. _____

5. Things seem to be working out very well. _____

6. In just a few more hours. _____

7. The ship sent out an S.O.S. lifeboats were lowered then it sank. _____

What is the third part of a friendly letter? _____

After each sentence, add correct punctuation; then write _declarative, interrogative, imperative,_ or _exclamatory._

1. Is this ever going to end__ _____   3. No, it can't be__ _____

2. Go find your sister__ _____   4. I'm dressing now__ _____

Put one kind of punctuation in each sentence below, and write the name of the punctuation on the line to the right.
These are your choices:

| period (.) | exclamation mark (!) | colon (:) | quotation marks (" ") |
| comma (,) | question mark (?) | semicolon (;) | apostrophe (') |

1. Will you be my Valentine _____

2. Today was a bad day let's hope tomorrow will be better. _____

3. There are too many starving people in the world _____

4. Send me these items a blanket, warm socks, and mittens. _____

(continued)

5. Yes, yes, it's she _____

6. Can I see your ring? she asked.

   Yes, you can, he replied. _____

7. Chriss jacket cost fifty dollars on sale. _____

8. I'm thinking of going to the party but it may be too late. _____

9. Its going to be a difficult exam. _____

10. Please close the door _____

In each word below, circle the prefix, and write the full meaning of the word on the line to the right.

1. disqualify _____

2. antislavery _____

3. unearthly _____

4. mistype _____

5. biannual _____

6. intercity _____

Use numbers to show alphabetical order.

____ ironic   ____ irony   ____ iron   ____ idle   ____ iambic   ____ isle   ____ idiot

Use diagonal lines to divide the following words into syllables.

1. silliness

2. kettle

3. secretive

4. prayerful

5. sensitive

6. employment

Label the following pairs of words *synonyms* or *antonyms*.

1. hire/fire _____

2. brutal/harsh _____

Every sentence must have at least one verb. Verbs are *action* words or *being* words. Some being words are *is, are, am, was, were.*

Underline the verbs in the following sentences. The number in parenthesis at the end of each sentence tells you how many verbs are in that sentence.

1. She <u>ran</u> quickly along the street. (1)

2. They <u>were</u> silly today. (1)

3. Kim <u>peeked</u> around the corner and <u>grinned</u> at her friend. (2)

4. The house burned down last night. (1)

5. Her brand new bicycle crashed into the fence. (1)

6. The cat looked at the mouse and walked away. (2)

7. They called the police. (1)

8. He dreamed about sheep. (1)

9. She typed a long letter. (1)

10. The city was too crowded for them. (1)

11. The lion roared and leaped toward the men. (2)

12. They got on the train in Boston and got off in New York. (2)

13. The rain fell all day and finally stopped in the evening. (2)

14. The knife dripped with blood after the hunter stabbed the tiger. (2)

15. He greedily ate the cheeseburger and then munched on his French fries. (2)

16. The plane flew across the Atlantic in record time and landed in London. (2)

17. The lady dressed and called a taxi. (2)

18. He packed his suitcase, walked to the door, and decided not to leave. (3)

19. The telephone rang, and she ran across the room and answered it. (3)

20. The bird sang beautifully, hovered in the air, and then flew away. (3)

What is a noun?_____

What is a verb?_____

Put an *N* under the nouns and a *V* under the verbs in the next two sentences.

1. The arrow flew through the air.

2. Her grandfather died on Saturday; the family buried him in Washington, D.C.

Every sentence must have at least one verb. Remember: verbs are *action* words or *being* words. Common being words are *is, are, am, was, were.*

Underline the verbs in the following sentences. The number in parenthesis at the end of each sentence tells you how many verbs are in that sentence.

1. The snake <u>bit</u> him on the leg. (1)

2. The plane <u>was</u> two hours late. (1)

3. Susan's hair <u>grew</u> fast; soon she <u>needed</u> another haircut. (2)

4. The ice cube melted quickly. (1)

5. The car screeched to a halt. (1)

6. The man was unhappy about the news. (1)

7. They played checkers for hours and hours. (1)

8. The train traveled two hundred miles overnight. (1)

9. The math paper is easy. (1)

10. The dishes crashed to the floor and splintered into hundreds of tiny pieces. (2)

11. The telephone rang fifteen times before she woke up. (2)

12. Trucks make lots of noise and pollution. (1)

13. She threw the pencil down on the floor and walked out of the room. (2)

14. The light shone in his eyes. (1)

15. She felt the spider on her leg. (1)

16. 375 people died in an air crash near Paris. (1)

17. The boy refused to take the spelling test. (1)

18. His report card was all A's. (1)

19. She stapled together her papers and handed them to the teacher. (2)

20. The woman talked so fast that no one understood her. (2)

In the following sentences, put an *N* under the nouns (people, places, and things) and a *V* under the verbs.

1. Smoke belched from the chimney.

2. The typewriter broke, so George took it to the repair shop.

3. The clouds cleared and the sun shone through.

4. A bomb exploded and wrecked the building.

What is a verb?_____

What is a noun?_____

Verbs are action words or being words (*is, are, am, was, were*). Underline the verbs in the following sentences. Some sentences contain more than one verb.

1. Her feet <u>got</u> cold.

2. He <u>was</u> the fastest runner in the camp.

3. The test began at eleven o'clock in the morning.

4. The little dog scampered across the street.

5. The drunk man lurched down the stairs.

6. The puzzles are too hard.

7. The ambulance raced through the streets toward the hospital.

8. They lived on the third floor of a brick apartment building.

9. There were only ten people in the classroom on that snowy day.

10. Some people think that storks deliver babies.

11. The plane started up its engines, took off, and flew to San Francisco.

12. The Chinese built a great wall around part of their country.

In the following sentences, fill in a verb of your own.

1. The car _____ around the corner at eighty miles an hour.

2. The boxer _____ his opponent in the jaw.

3. It wasn't long before the boat _____.

4. She _____ fifteen years old.

5. All of a sudden the girl _____.

6. The boy _____ sick after he _____ too much spaghetti.

In each sentence below, put an *N* under the nouns and a *V* under the verbs.

1. The house was bright yellow; lots of people noticed it.

2. The plant grew until it covered the side of the house.

3. She married a man with blue eyes.

Underline the verbs in the following sentences. Some sentences contain more than one verb.

1. She <u>said</u> that she <u>wanted</u> some dessert.

2. The fire destroyed the entire building.

3. His father quit his job and looked for another one.

4. The carpenter hollered when he hammered his own thumb.

5. The submarine sank to the bottom of the ocean.

6. The eagle soared in the air, and then dove to the ground when it spotted its prey.

7. The ruler was twelve inches long.

8. When she first heard the story, she believed it.

9. The telephone wire snapped in the storm and fell to the ground.

10. The gorilla pounded its chest and swung from the tree.

11. The baby lion is very cute.

12. The ice cream was delicious, but it melted very fast on such a hot day.

Now make up some sentences of your own. Underline all the verbs in them.

1. Write one with one verb.

   _____

2. Write one with two verbs.

   _____

3. Write one with three verbs.

   _____

Now put an _N_ under the nouns and a _V_ under the verbs in the sentences below.

1. The woman looked in the dictionary and found the right word.

2. His uncle was a factory worker in Detroit.

3. The sharp knife cut his finger, so he put a Band-Aid on it.

4. The hunters trapped the antelope and shot it.

5. The dog drove the neighbors crazy because it barked in the night.

6. The chocolate was delicious.

Underline the verbs in the following sentences. Some sentences will contain more than one verb. Check your work. There are twenty-five verbs in the sentences below.

1. Jacqueline shook her head.

2. The boat hit the dock at high speed.

3. Some people think that guns are very dangerous.

4. They heard the train in the distance.

5. She stopped her work and ran to the telephone.

6. The police caught the escaped convict after they chased him for ten hours.

7. The calculator solved the problem in a second.

8. He read a book and then wrote a long letter to his mother.

9. She dreamed that she was queen for a day.

10. Some people think the end of the world is at hand.

11. The tiger chased the zebra and caught it.

12. The fire burned fiercely for an hour before they put it out.

13. Her scissors cut through the wire.

14. It was a cold, foggy day in December.

15. The steamroller flattened the dirt and smoothed the ground for the road.

16. His new minibike is a lemon.

Write the plurals of each of the following nouns.

1. man _____
5. mass _____
9. tax _____

2. child _____
6. army _____
10. house _____

3. ox _____
7. mouse _____
11. lash _____

4. leaf _____
8. fish _____
12. potato _____

Write four proper nouns.

1. _____
2. _____
3. _____
4. _____

Circle the correct homonyms in the following sentences.

1. (There / their / they're) grandmother lived over (there / their / they're).

2. It is much (to / two / too) early to know whether she won (to / two / too) prizes.

Label the following pairs of words *synonyms* or *antonyms*.

1. copy/reproduce _____
2. meticulous/careful _____

Use numbers to show alphabetical order.

____ short   ____ shop   ____ shifty   ____ simmer   ____ sample   ____ shove   ____ shone

Use diagonal lines to divide the following words into syllables.

1. gallstones   2. popover   3. penniless   4. pontiff   5. checkbook   6. incredible

Circle the suffixes in the following words.

1. taxation   2. nationality   3. happiness   4. communism   5. childlike   6. breakable

In each word below, circle the prefix and write the full meaning of the word on the line.

1. superwoman _____
4. postmortem _____

2. interracial _____
5. misspell _____

3. dislike _____
6. indecisive _____

Put one kind of punctuation in each sentence below, and write the name of the punctuation on the line to the right.

These are your choices:

| period (.) | exclamation mark (!) | colon (:) | quotation marks (" ") |
| comma (,) | question mark (?) | semicolon (;) | apostrophe (') |

1. The woman stood and said, I don't understand what you're saying. _____

2. Kyle had three hobbies stamp collecting, skiing, and building model airplanes. _____

(continued)

3. Im not going to listen to that music any more. _____

4. Some days it rains other days it is just cloudy. _____

5. I'm so excited _____

6. Come visit me sometime _____

7. When did the fire begin _____

8. Now Luke you have to help your grandmother. _____

9. They stayed at Dorothys house until the storm passed. _____

10. Brazil is the largest country in South America _____

Put capitals in the right places.

1. the pope lives in rome, italy, and worships god daily.

2. the letter began, "dear mr. president, i hope you're well."

Label the groups of words below *fragment, slang, double negative, run-on, needs capitals, needs punctuation,* **or** *O.K.*

1. That dag-nab tractor keeps copping out on me. _____

2. The dictionary, a book with many meanings. _____

3. Come here make it quick I have to talk to you. _____

4. It's better to be safe than sorry. _____

5. Don't go nowhere without your wallet. _____

6. she didn't see the train coming. _____

The past tense of a verb is the way you say or write it when the action has happened in the past (before now).

Write the past tense of each verb. Follow the rule if there is one.

For many verbs, just add *ed*.

1. walk ___walked___
2. talk _____
3. look _____
4. pick _____
5. chew _____
6. paint _____
7. roll _____

For verbs ending in *e*, just add *d*.

1. dance ___danced___
2. hate _____
3. bounce _____

For verbs ending in *y*, usually change the y to i and add *ed*.

1. try ___tried___
2. cry _____
3. dry _____

For some verbs ending in a single consonant, double the consonant and add *ed*.

1. hop ___hopped___
2. chop _____
3. stab _____

But many verbs are just plain crazy, and you just have to remember their past tense. If you don't know some of these, be sure to ask your teacher about them, and then learn them.

1. am ___was___
2. blow _____
3. buy _____
4. bring _____
5. build _____
6. break _____
7. bleed _____
8. bite _____
9. come _____
10. catch _____
11. cut _____
12. draw _____

13. drink _____
14. do _____
15. dive _____
16. drive _____
17. eat _____
18. feel _____
19. fight _____
20. fly _____
21. fall _____
22. grow _____
23. go _____
24. give _____

25. get _____
26. have _____
27. hit _____
28. hear _____
29. is _____
30. know _____
31. leave _____
32. meet _____
33. make _____
34. run _____
35. ring _____

Past Tense of Verbs 2

Write the past tense of each of the following verbs. Each group in the first column follows a rule. The rest are crazy.

1. spank _spanked_

2. leak _____

3. look _____

4. walk _____

5. prance _pranced_

6. glance _____

7. hate _____

8. bounce _____

9. try _tried_

10. cry _____

11. dry _____

12. hop _hopped_

13. chop _____

14. dip _____

15. jam _____

16. pin _____

17. drop _____

18. sip _____

19. rob _____

20. shop _____

21. stop _____

22. grab _____

23. ride _rode_

24. read _____

25. shrink _____

26. sing _____

27. sweep _____

28. sit _____

29. sleep _____

30. send _____

31. see _____

32. swim _____

33. speak _____

34. stick _____

35. sink _____

36. shoot _____

37. stand _____

38. shine _____

39. sting _____

40. say _____

41. throw _____

42. teach _____

43. think _____

44. tell _____

45. write _____

46. take _____

47. tear _____

48. wear _____

49. weave _____

50. weep _____

51. wind _____

Write the past tense of each verb. Be sure to ask your teacher about any you're not sure of, so you can learn them all.

1. crawl _____	26. dive _____	51. sweep _____
2. watch _____	27. drive _____	52. sit _____
3. wax _____	28. eat _____	53. sleep _____
4. fake _____	29. feel _____	54. send _____
5. waste _____	30. fight _____	55. see _____
6. wave _____	31. fly _____	56. swim _____
7. dry _____	32. fall _____	57. speak _____
8. marry _____	33. grow _____	58. stick _____
9. stab _____	34. go _____	59. sink _____
10. rob _____	35. give _____	60. shoot _____
11. pin _____	36. get _____	61. stand _____
12. am _____	37. have _____	62. shine _____
13. blow _____	38. hit _____	63. sting _____
14. buy _____	39. hear _____	64. say _____
15. bring _____	40. is _____	65. throw _____
16. build _____	41. know _____	66. take _____
17. break _____	42. leave _____	67. teach _____
18. bleed _____	43. meet _____	68. tear _____
19. bite _____	44. make _____	69. think _____
20. come _____	45. run _____	70. tell _____
21. catch _____	46. ring _____	71. wear _____
22. cut _____	47. ride _____	72. weave _____
23. draw _____	48. read _____	73. write _____
24. drink _____	49. shrink _____	74. weep _____
25. do _____	50. sing _____	75. wind _____

Write the past tense of each verb below.

1. draw _____
2. buy _____
3. pick _____
4. bounce _____
5. hop _____
6. bring _____
7. leave _____
8. have _____
9. stick _____
10. chop _____
11. cry _____
12. work _____
13. give _____
14. meet _____
15. eat _____
16. do _____
17. sweep _____
18. sting _____
19. shoot _____
20. hear _____
21. build _____
22. look _____
23. paste _____
24. bite _____
25. marry _____
26. come _____
27. hit _____

28. sink _____
29. say _____
30. ride _____
31. cut _____
32. catch _____
33. am _____
34. blow _____
35. hate _____
36. rob _____
37. dive _____
38. grow _____
39. fly _____
40. run _____
41. is _____
42. stand _____
43. throw _____
44. wind _____
45. tell _____
46. send _____
47. read _____
48. drink _____
49. break _____
50. write _____
51. teach _____
52. tear _____
53. shine _____
54. bleed _____

55. pin _____
56. weave _____
57. weep _____
58. speak _____
59. sing _____
60. make _____
61. know _____
62. think _____
63. ring _____
64. fall _____
65. drive _____
66. get _____
67. wear _____
68. swim _____
69. sit _____
70. take _____
71. see _____
72. fight _____
73. feel _____
74. go _____
75. sleep _____
76. shrink _____
77. sip _____
78. dry _____
79. crack _____
80. watch _____

Write the past tense of each verb below.

1. sink _____
2. say _____
3. ride _____
4. cut _____
5. catch _____
6. am _____
7. blow _____
8. hate _____
9. rob _____
10. dive _____
11. grow _____
12. fly _____
13. run _____
14. is _____
15. stand _____
16. throw _____
17. wind _____
18. tell _____
19. send _____
20. read _____
21. drink _____
22. break _____
23. write _____
24. teach _____
25. tear _____
26. shine _____
27. bleed _____

28. draw _____
29. buy _____
30. pick _____
31. bounce _____
32. hop _____
33. bring _____
34. leave _____
35. have _____
36. stick _____
37. chop _____
38. cry _____
39. work _____
40. give _____
41. meet _____
42. eat _____
43. do _____
44. sweep _____
45. sting _____
46. shoot _____
47. hear _____
48. build _____
49. look _____
50. paste _____
51. bite _____
52. marry _____
53. come _____
54. hit _____

55. pin _____
56. weave _____
57. weep _____
58. speak _____
59. sing _____
60. make _____
61. know _____
62. think _____
63. ring _____
64. fall _____
65. drive _____
66. get _____
67. wear _____
68. swim _____
69. sit _____
70. take _____
71. see _____
72. fight _____
73. feel _____
74. go _____
75. sleep _____
76. shrink _____
77. sip _____
78. dry _____
79. crack _____
80. watch _____

Circle the nouns and underline the verbs in the following sentences.

1. The old horse galloped slowly toward the barn.

2. The actress danced and sang through the night.

3. The army attacked the city, and the enemy surrendered.

Write the plurals of the following nouns.

1. dancer_____   5. tomato_____   9. deer_____

2. wife_____   6. foot_____   10. half_____

3. tooth_____   7. valley_____   11. match_____

4. party_____   8. fox_____   12. child_____

In the following sentences, circle the correct homonyms.

1. It's not sensible (to / two / too) drink (to / two / too) much.

2. (There / their / they're) not thinking about (there / their / they're) future plans.

Label the following pairs of words _antonyms_ or _homonyms_.

1. perilous/safe _____   2. active/indolent _____

Use numbers to show alphabetical order.

_____ bell   _____ beef   _____ brother   _____ butter   _____ bellicose   _____ butcher   _____ bright

Use diagonal lines to divide the following words into syllables.

1. saturate   3. simpleminded   5. briefcase

2. matchless   4. bravery   6. battle

In the following words, circle the suffixes.

1. cleanly   2. reasonably   3. momentous   4. awfully   5. courageous   6. basement

For each word below, circle the prefix, and write the meaning of the full word on the line.

1. trilingual _____   4. redo _____

2. microbus _____   5. untested _____

3. anti-German _____   6. misconduct _____

Underline a subject once and a predicate twice.

1. The man in the blue suede cap robbed the bank, and the police couldn't catch him.

(continued)

Review Test 28

Label each group of words *fragment, slang, double negative, run-on, needs capitals, needs punctuation,* or *O.K.*

1. Don't give us no interference. _____

2. is that you knocking on the door? _____

3. After the three-hour game. _____

4. She always whistled on her way to work. _____

5. He asked, Why don't you pay her a decent salary? _____

6. It ain't no use wondering about that. _____

7. She left a few minutes later she was back she apologized. _____

Use numbers to show the correct order for the seven parts of a business letter.

____ Body of Letter   ____ Signature   ____ Date   ____ Salutation

____ Your Address   ____ Closing   ____ Name and Address of Addressee

What is the third part of a friendly letter? _____

Use apostrophes to show possession.

1. car/woman _____   2. house/boys _____

83

Every verb has several tenses. The tenses of some verbs have been given to you in the lines below. Use these as models to fill in the tenses for the other verbs. Use either *he* or *she* as a subject.

	Verb	Present Tense	Past Tense	Present Perfect Tense	Future Tense
1.	blow	he blows	he blew	he has blown	he will blow
2.	sing	she sings	she sang	she has sung	she will sing
3.	go	he goes	he went	he has gone	he will go
4.	am	she is	she was	she has been	she will be
5.	play				
6.	ring				
7.	hear				
8.	talk				
9.	run				
10.	throw				
11.	leave				

On the lines below, write sentences in the other verb tenses. Change just the verb.

1. Present Tense ___She sings that song very well.___

2. Past Tense _____

3. Present Perfect Tense _____

4. Future Tense _____

1. Present Tense ___She walks to the store very quickly.___

2. Past Tense _____

3. Present Perfect Tense _____

4. Future Tense _____

Write in the tenses of the verbs below. Some have been done for you as models. Use either *he* or *she* as a subject.

Verb	Present Tense (Progressive Form)	Past Tense	Present Perfect Tense	Future Tense
1. bring	she is bringing	she brought	she has brought	she will bring
2. have	he is having	he had	he has had	he will have
3. dance				
4. look				
5. leave				
6. make				
7. sing				
8. think				
9. save				
10. watch				
11. chop				
12. drop				
13. cut				
14. do				
15. fall				
16. sweep				

Now write the sentences below in the three other tenses. Change just the verb.

1. Present Tense (Progressive Form) He is flying a green kite.

2. Past Tense _____

3. Present Perfect Tense _____

4. Future Tense _____

1. Present Tense (Progressive Form) He is reading a terrific book.

2. Past Tense _____

3. Present Perfect Tense _____

4. Future Tense _____

Write in the tenses of the verbs below. Some have been done for you to use as models. Use either *he* or *she* as a subject.

Verb	Present Tense (Progressive Form)	Past Tense	Present Perfect Tense	Future Tense
1. ring	she is ringing	she rang	she has rung	she will ring
2. drink	he is drinking	he drank	he has drunk	he will drink
3. run				
4. catch				
5. build				
6. pick				
7. stab				
8. waste				
9. give				
10. sink				
11. say				
12. throw				
13. teach				

Now write the sentences below in the other verb tenses. Change just the verb.

1. Present Tense (Progressive Form) She is running like the wind.

2. Past Tense

3. Present Perfect Tense

4. Future Tense

1. Present Tense (Progressive Form)

2. Past Tense

3. Present Perfect Tense

4. Future Tense He will sing the song one more time.

Write in the other tenses of the verbs below. Use / as the subject.

Verb	Present Tense (Progressive Form)	Past Tense	Present Perfect Tense	Future Tense
1. bite	I am biting	I bit	I have bitten	I will bite
2. paint				
3. jam				
4. grow				
5. feel				
6. do				
7. sing				
8. see				
9. tell				
10. think				
11. say				
12. give				
13. break				

Now write the sentences below in the other verb tenses. Change just the verb.

1. Present Tense (Progressive Form) _____

2. Past Tense ___ I wrote a long letter to my girlfriend. _____

3. Present Perfect Tense _____

4. Future Tense _____

1. Present Tense (Progressive Form) _____

2. Past Tense _____

3. Present Perfect Tense _____

4. Future Tense ___ I will buy six cans of coke. _____

Write the verbs below in the other tenses.

Verb	Present Tense (Progressive Form)	Past Tense	Present Perfect Tense	Future Tense
1. give	I am giving	I gave	I have given	I will give
2. think				
3. tell				
4. paint				
5. drop				
6. break				
7. say				
8. run				
9. go				
10. sing				
11. hear				

Now write the sentences below in the other verb tenses. Change just the verbs.

1. Present Tense (Progressive Form) _____

2. Past Tense ____ The rocket shot into the sky. _____

3. Present Perfect Tense _____

4. Future Tense _____

1. Present Tense (Progressive Form) ____ She is drinking a glass of milk. _____

2. Past Tense _____

3. Present Perfect Tense _____

4. Future Tense _____

Each group of words below has *one* thing wrong with it. Correct the mistake and write on the line what the problem was. One group is correct.
Choose from this list:

sentence fragment	needs apostrophe to show possession
slang	needs apostrophe to make a contraction
double negative	needs comma
run-on sentence	needs colon
needs period	needs semicolon
needs question mark	wrong use of *to/two/too*
needs exclamation mark	wrong use of *there/their/they're*
needs capitals	no problem
needs quotation marks	

1. Oh no, it can't be true _____

2. She jumped to her feet she smiled she cried. _____

3. They were the only to people in the room. _____

4. Why are you looking at me that way _____

5. His rich uncle living in Canada. _____

6. don't you think i care about you? _____

7. This isnt the first time youve been warned. _____

8. That group got a whole lot of soul. _____

9. Sheila come here for a minute. _____

10. The skyscraper was almost finished. _____

11. I appreciate that, said the woman. It's very nice of you. _____

12. Can't you never call me? _____

13. There house was the fanciest on the street. _____

14. The White House is the presidents residence. _____

15. I hope to be three things poet, painter, and sculptor. _____

16. They drove for an hour to reach the cemetery _____

17. Some meals are good other meals are terrible. _____

Write the past tense of the following verbs.

1. look _____	6. am _____	11. come _____
2. chop _____	7. build _____	12. fall _____
3. meet _____	8. fight _____	13. drink _____
4. eat _____	9. cry _____	14. bite _____
5. bounce _____	10. bleed _____	15. go _____

(continued)

Review Test 29

Write the plurals of the following nouns.

1. ox _____
2. lady _____
3. calf _____
4. foot _____

5. monkey _____
6. life _____
7. goose _____
8. wish _____

9. boy _____
10. dance _____
11. tax _____
12. deer _____

Label the following pairs *synonyms, antonyms,* or *homonyms.*

1. peaceful/bellicose _____

2. dew/due _____

3. repay/reimburse _____

Pronouns take the place of nouns to name people, places, and things.
Here are the most common pronouns:

he	she	it	they	you	we	I
him	her	its	them	your	us	me
his	hers		their	yours	our	my
			theirs		ours	mine

In the following sentences, write the correct pronouns under the underlined words. The first sentence has been done for you.

1. The man called the girl; the girl didn't want to come to the man.
      He   her   she   him.

2. The boys were thinking of giving the turtle to the woman.

3. Marilyn's spelling paper was perfect; Marilyn got an A on the paper.

4. You and I must go to see the circus with John and Leroy.

5. Susan and Karen put the puzzle together and showed it to the teacher.

6. Julie played jump rope with the new girl.

7. That dog is yours and mine.

8. That ball is Troy and Maurice's.

9. The car's engine was not working, but the mechanic fixed the engine.

10. That was Henry's minibike, not Susan's.

11. That game belongs to (your name).

12. (Your name) is not feeling very well.

13. The policeman's car stalled in traffic, and the policeman didn't get to the party.

14. The man called his brother's store.

15. That is Dorothy's.

16. The car's headlights were not working, so the men didn't see the car coming.

Remember the pronouns:

he	she	it	they	you	we	I
him	her	its	them	your	us	me
his	hers		their	yours	our	my
			theirs		ours	mine

In the following sentences, put the correct pronouns under the underlined words. Then read over the whole sentence to make sure it sounds right. The first sentence has been done for you.

1. His mother's birthday was on Sunday; his father's birthday was on Tuesday.
   Her   his

2. Mary Ann and Brenda put the books back on the shelf.

3. You and I went to see the boys about some important business.

4. It was Ronald's turn on the game, but Helena didn't want to give the game up.

5. It is time for you and me to go home.

6. That is Stacey and Teresa's table, but Robert insists on sitting there.

7. Why don't you talk to the teacher about the problem.

8. The typewriter's ribbon was all worn out.

9. The typewriter's ribbon was all worn out.

10. The man's muscles were like jelly.

11. That was Felicia's best work, but Mr. Brown didn't like it.

12. Two hundred policemen were picketing in front of City Hall.

13. That jet was the president's, and the president often used it.

14. That basketball game belongs to (your name).

15. That is George and Harold's bicycle, but Karen wants a ride on the bicycle.

Pronouns 3

In the following sentences, write the correct pronouns under the underlined words.

1. The old lady wanted to get married to the young college student.

2. David's pencil was stolen, but David found the pencil under the table.

3. That was the boy's basketball.

4. That was the boys' basketball.

5. You and I didn't see the three girls hiding behind the locker.

6. The girl's muscles were bigger than (your name's).

7. The girls' game lasted longer than yours and mine.

8. The police came to see the men about the robbery.

9. The paper was Susie's, but Darvin took the paper and gave it to Mr. Mariani.

10. Sharon's picture was so beautiful that the teachers put the picture in the art show.

11. Raymond and Darryl came to see Cynthia about the lost books.

12. (Your name) hollered like crazy, and Aaron joined right in with (your name).

13. The soldiers fought long and hard to capture the little hill.

In the following sentences, put the right pronouns under the underlined words.

1. Why don't <u>you and I</u> go to visit <u>Sharon and Ted's</u> house?

2. There is a place where <u>Johnnie</u> can go to find <u>his girlfriend</u>.

3. The <u>light</u> burned out, and <u>Carolyn</u> had to change <u>the light</u>.

4. <u>The two houses</u> caught on fire, and <u>his mother</u> called the fire department.

5. <u>The two men</u> came to see <u>you and me</u> last Monday.

6. The <u>teacher</u> liked <u>Henry</u>, but he liked <u>Margaret</u> better still.

7. Morning is <u>the girls'</u> gym time, not <u>the boys'</u>.

8. That is <u>the girl's</u> book, not <u>the boy's</u>.

9. Don't you see <u>those three boys</u> running toward <u>you and me</u>?

10. That is <u>Edwin and Kenneth's</u> locker, and (<u>your name</u>) told you not to use <u>that locker</u>.

In the following sentences, write *N* under the nouns, *V* under the verbs, and *PRO* under the pronouns.

1. The car arrived at their house at night.

2. Her brother talked to him about the TV show.

3. We wrote to our mother, and she sent us some money.

Put the right pronouns under the underlined words in the following sentences.

1. <u>The car's</u> bumper was all smashed up after <u>the man</u> drove into the wall.

2. <u>The play</u> was fun to watch, but <u>you and I</u> didn't think <u>the play</u> was the best ever.

3. <u>The young woman</u> was kidnapped by <u>three men</u> and held for ransom.

4. <u>That ball</u> is <u>Brenda's</u>, but <u>John</u> says it belongs to <u>John</u>.

5. <u>(Your name)</u> can't figure out what is wrong with <u>(your name)</u>.

6. That is <u>Edwin's and Lolethia's</u> work, not <u>yours and mine</u>.

7. Here is <u>the girl's</u> bicycle.

8. Here is <u>the girls'</u> bicycle.

9. <u>The policemen</u> came to see <u>Charlie</u> about <u>Mary's</u> typewriter.

10. <u>That dog</u> is <u>Helen's</u>.

11. <u>The men's poker game</u> lasted all night, and <u>the men's</u> wives were furious.

Correct the mistake in each group of words below. Write the problem on the line to the right. One group is correct.
Choose from this list:

sentence fragment
slang
double negative
run-on sentence
needs period
needs question mark
needs exclamation mark
needs capitals
needs quotation marks

needs apostrophe (for possession)
needs apostrophe (in contraction)
needs comma
needs colon
needs semicolon
wrong use of *to / two / too*
wrong use of *there / their / they're*
no problem

1. What is the sense in going _____

2. Davids mother was in bad shape. _____

3. There is to much noise in this room. _____

4. Her father. A man of integrity. _____

5. The newspaper was printed late at night. _____

6. He asked, Is this the way to San Diego? _____

7. I don't think neither of them did it, officer. _____

8. The engine sputtered a few minutes later it died. _____

9. Good grief, it's finally happening _____

10. This blasted test is giving me a pain in the neck. _____

11. "Don't forget the present" she said. _____

12. the trip to mexico city was a great success. _____

13. I'm coming stop worrying I'll be there in a minute. _____

14. Whats the trouble down there? _____

15. If you look over their you'll see the Big Dipper. _____

16. Remember three things your lunch, your textbook, and a pencil. _____

17. Get going _____

Use diagonal lines to divide the following words into syllables.

1. orderly   2. signify   3. ambulance   4. towering   5. brittle   6. medicine

Use numbers to show alphabetical order.

____ triumph   ____ trap   ____ taper   ____ towel   ____ trumpet   ____ tried   ____ top   ____ tire

(continued)

Review Test 30

Circle the suffixes.

1. capital*ism*　　2. loud*ly*　　3. rest*ive*　　4. dread*ful*　　5. like*ness*　　6. self*less*　　7. rac*ism*

Circle the prefixes, and write the full meaning of each word on each line to the right.

1. *pre*-exam _____

4. *ex*-president _____

2. *non*profit _____

5. *mini*bike _____

3. *post*graduate _____

6. *trans*continental _____

Label the following sentence *declarative, interrogative, imperative,* or *exclamatory.*

1. Go fetch that football. _____

After each word, write the long or short vowel sound that it makes.

1. fe*a*ther __　2. r*a*ke __　3. w*i*ndow __　4. p*e*ncil __　5. l*ea*p __　6. m*i*le __　7. tri*u*mph __　8. r*u*g __

Write four proper nouns.

1. _____　2. _____　3. _____　4. _____

What is the third part of a friendly letter? _____

What do you do to the first word in a paragraph? _____

Adjectives describe people, places, or things. In each group of words below, underline the adjective, write *ADJ* under it, and draw an arrow to the word it describes.

1. an <u>old</u> cow
   ADJ

2. an understanding mother

3. the new bicycle

4. the sickening sight

5. that unbelievable story

6. the latest news

7. her funny uncle

8. a terrible smell

---

9. The car was <u>beautiful.</u>
   ADJ

10. a woman who is clever

11. a typewriter that is broken

12. the boy who was smartest

13. The meal was disgusting.

14. a story which is scary

15. the scissors which were sharp

16. a smell that was evocative

---

17. the <u>new</u>, <u>exciting</u>, <u>unforgettable</u> movie
    ADJ   ADJ   ADJ

18. her beautiful, attractive, vivacious mother

19. The man was strong, handsome, honest, and kind.

20. The house was large, spooky, and forbidding.

Adjectives 2

Adjectives are words that describe people, places, or things.

An adjective can be right next to the word it describes. (The *red* house.)

An adjective also can come later in the sentence. (The house was *red*.)

There can be several adjectives describing one word. (There was an *old, ugly, red* house on the street.)

In the following sentences, write *ADJ* under the adjectives, and draw arrows to the pronouns or nouns they describe. The number in parenthesis at the end of the sentence tells you how many adjectives are in that sentence.

1. The old man came into the dark room. (2)
   ADJ   ADJ

2. She wore a pretty dress to the party. (1)

3. The green car smashed into the red bus. (2)

4. Her cat was sick, so she took it to the nearest hospital. (2)

5. The new knife was sharp. (2)

6. That girl is beautiful, smart, and charming. (3)

7. New York is a busy, noisy, violent, and crowded city. (4)

8. Her new clothes were burned in the terrible fire. (2)

9. He wrote a long letter to his favorite girlfriend. (2)

10. The sky was blue and orange during the spectacular sunset. (3)

11. That was a dry joke. (1)

12. The plant was green and yellow and red. (3)

Remember: adjectives describe people, places, and things.

In the following sentences, write *ADJ* under the adjectives, and draw arrows to the nouns or pronouns they describe. The number in parenthesis at the end of the sentence tells you how many adjectives are in that sentence.

1. They robbed the poor, old, lame woman. (3)
   ADJ ADJ ADJ

2. The young boy walked along the quiet street. (2)

3. He wore a blue sweater and a red coat to the party. (2)

4. She was beautiful, and he loved her at first sight. (2)

5. The yellow car won an important race. (2)

6. The boy was unhappy because they stole his new, expensive bicycle. (3)

7. Those were the most disgusting, revolting, putrid, sickening beans I have ever tasted! (4)

8. His grades on the latest report card were excellent. (2)

9. The scissors were sharp, and they cut right through the thick paper. (2)

10. The typewriter was broken, so they wrote the paper in black ink. (2)

Now think of as many adjectives as you can to describe the following words.

1. a policeman _____

   _____

2. yourself _____

   _____

3. a race car _____

   _____

What is an adjective? _____

What is a noun? _____

What is a verb? _____

What is a pronoun? _____

In the following sentences, write *ADJ* under the adjectives, and draw arrows to the nouns or pronouns which the adjectives describe.

1. He earned a large salary working in the local supermarket.

2. The clock was broken, so she missed the appointment with her favorite dentist.

3. The meat was rotten, so they had to eat that awful spaghetti.

4. The same old tired people kept coming to the grubby racetrack.

5. The corridors were dark and silent at night.

6. The woman was angry and disgusted to hear the bad news.

7. That girl is slick, beautiful, charming, smart, and lovable.

8. The thin, hungry dog looked for a tasty meal.

9. The game was long but exciting.

In the following sentences, put *N* under the nouns, *V* under the verbs, *PRO* under the pronouns, and *ADJ* under the adjectives.

1. The old man talked to me.

2. The fast train passed our car.

3. His sick grandmother was unhappy.

4. Their new house was beautiful.

In the following sentences, underline the adjectives, write *ADJ* under each one, and draw arrows to the nouns or pronouns they describe.

1. They bought a new car.

2. The black horse ran through the open gate.

3. It was early morning when the unexpected visitor arrived.

4. The latest newspaper reported the terrible earthquake.

5. She was happy but uneasy.

6. The problem was long and complicated.

7. The city was quiet and peaceful and deserted late at night.

8. Her spelling grade was terrible, but her math grade was terrific.

9. The loud, obnoxious announcer told the huge crowd to quiet down.

10. She is the most beautiful girl I have ever met.

Correct the mistake in each group of words and write the problem on the line to the right. One is correct.

Choose from this list:

sentence fragment	needs apostrophe to show possession
slang	needs apostrophe to make a contraction
double negative	needs comma
run-on sentence	needs colon
needs period	needs semicolon
needs question mark	wrong use of *to/two/too*
needs exclamation mark	wrong use of *there/their/they're*
needs capitals	no problem
needs quotation marks	

1. This is a stickup! Don't nobody move! _____

2. Can you see what I mean Mark? _____

3. Seeing the blind man made him feel lucky to have to eyes. _____

4. Cruising through the town looking for trouble. _____

5. Their trip to canada lasted two days. _____

6. Dont tell me youve won first prize. _____

7. It's a wonder you can walk after that meal. _____

8. You ain't coming with me, and that's that. _____

9. Can I see that ring? she begged. I promise I won't lose it. _____

10. Here are your instructions go east two miles, then proceed west one mile. _____

11. The sky was a lovely blue _____

12. The train is coming off the rails _____

13. Lightning struck the tree a few days later it fell down. _____

14. The mens club didn't allow women inside. _____

15. Is this the last train to New York _____

16. There going to need lots of help on that job. _____

17. The Yankees won the Red Sox lost the fans were delighted. _____

Write the sentences below in three other verb tenses. Change just the verb.

Present	Past Tense	Present Perfect Tense	Future Tense
1. I run			
2. I catch			
3. I sing			
4. He goes			

(continued)

Review Test 31

Write the plural of the following nouns.

1. table _____
2. shelf _____
3. jockey _____
4. wish _____

5. lady _____
6. tomato _____
7. fox _____
8. woman _____

9. pass _____
10. mouse _____
11. wife _____
12. tooth _____

Label the following pairs of words _synonyms, antonyms,_ or _homonyms._

1. scold/castigate _____

2. night/knight _____

Of the following words, circle the one that doesn't rhyme with the others.

1. through   2. brew   3. do   4. grew   5. though   6. drew

Use diagonal lines to divide the following words into syllables.

1. contender   2. barrier   3. constant   4. settlement   5. breakfasting

Use numbers to show alphabetical order.

_____ rigor   _____ raffle   _____ rumpled   _____ ripple   _____ raging   _____ rope   _____ rotten

Adverbs describe verbs and often answer the questions *how* or *when.* Many adverbs end in *ly*.

Underline the adverbs in the following sentences. The first two have been done for you.

1. The woman drove her car <u>quickly</u> down the street.

2. I will call him <u>now</u>.

3. Her mother shouted loudly out the back door for her to come into the house for dinner.

4. The plane roared deafeningly toward the runway.

5. The car sped wildly over the cliff.

6. They ran fast, so they won the race.

7. The light shone brightly in the darkness.

Adverbs also describe adjectives or other adverbs.
Underline these kinds of adverbs in the following sentences. The first two have been done for you.

1. It was a <u>very</u> hot day.

2. My sister skates <u>pretty</u> well.

3. The man was awfully handsome.

4. That was a really clever trick you pulled.

5. That was a very, very unkind thing to do to the poor dog.

6. She felt awfully bad about the death of her mother.

7. Everyone was really scared of the monster.

Now think up your own adverbs, and write them in the blanks below.

1. She screamed _____ as the man ran after her.

2. There goes a _____ beautiful person.

3. He finished the problems very _____ .

4. The sky was a _____ beautiful color.

5. The dog barked _____ after it was hit by the car.

6. It was a _____ dark night.

Adverbs 2

Remember: adverbs describe verbs and often answer the questions *how* or *when*. Many adverbs end in *ly*. Adverbs also can describe adjectives or other adverbs.

Underline the adverbs in the following sentences.

1. She walked slowly toward home after losing the game.

2. There was a terribly ugly gorilla at the zoo.

3. It was a very cloudy and stormy day.

4. The man was awfully mad about the broken window in his car.

5. The bomb exploded loudly and shattered windows miles away.

6. She was a very sick woman when they put her in the hospital.

7. He screamed piercingly as the doctor gave him the shot.

8. They walked straight to the policeman.

9. That happened yesterday.

10. The car was a really beautiful orange.

11. He was painfully aware of what he had to do.

12. It was a very difficult decision for President Kennedy to make.

13. She protested shrilly when the umpire called him out.

14. The lawyer made a very convincing argument.

15. Please tell me about your problems tomorrow.

16. The man was obviously drunk.

17. The man was driving too fast.

18. The man waited nervously as the judge made up his mind about the sentence.

19. The plane flew so fast that it arrived early.

20. The car swerved crazily around the corner and slammed into the lamp.

In the following sentences, fill in the blanks with adverbs.

1. Her father was a _____ good man.

2. The tiger _____ attacked the zebra.

3. Her uncle was _____ sick of the landlord's bothering him.

4. She was in a _____ bad mood yesterday.

Adverbs 3

Remember: adverbs describe verbs and often answer the questions *how* or *when.* Many adverbs end in *ly.* Adverbs also can describe adjectives or other adverbs.

Underline the adverbs in the following sentences. Some sentences contain more than one adverb.

1. She reached quickly into her purse and pulled out her comb.

2. The man reacted slowly to the joke.

3. She laughed hysterically when the comedian made fun of the president.

4. The car was very, very fast.

5. It was a terribly hot day in the middle of the summer.

6. He finally figured out the mystery later.

7. The train traveled fast and arrived early.

8. She got really sick of waiting for her brother who is always late.

9. The headlights shone brightly through the fog.

10. The monster moved menacingly toward the children.

11. Her grandfather was almost dead.

12. It was a really exciting book.

13. They had a delightfully beautiful day for the picnic.

14. She was a marvelously good swimmer.

15. He sang beautifully in the choir.

16. It will be too bad if you arrive late for the game.

17. I am awfully sorry about my mistake.

18. It's very good to see you again after all these years.

19. The ghost was almost invisible.

20. The tree was nearly split in two by the lightning.

Label each group of words below, *nouns, verbs, pronouns, adjectives,* or *adverbs.*

1. he, she, it, they, we, I, us, theirs _____

2. quickly, slowly, awfully, very, fast _____

3. man, boy, Henry, Chicago, beanstalk _____

4. cute, beautiful, sad, slow, ugly, mean _____

5. run, jump, throw, sing, sway, dream, race _____

Adverbs 4

Underline the adverbs in the following sentences. The number in parenthesis at the end of each sentence tells you how many adverbs are in that sentence.

1. She slept soundly and woke up late. (2)

2. The woman was awfully proud of her son when he got out of the army. (1)

3. The car drove too fast for the police to catch it. (2)

4. If you listen very carefully, you can hear the train in the distance. (2)

5. He smiled winningly and tried to get through the gate to the ball park. (1)

6. Slowly and silently, the commandos crept up on the enemy installation. (2)

7. The president reacted violently and profanely to the newspaper article. (2)

8. She acted silly, and her mother angrily sent her to her room. (2)

9. Abruptly the music stopped and the lights went out. (1)

10. It is very important that you behave well at the party. (2)

Now supply your own adverbs. Try to make them interesting!

1. The crowd reacted _____ when the football team won.

2. It is _____ important that we get there on time.

3. The woman was _____ smart.

4. If you keep acting _____ you will be punished.

5. The typewriter clattered _____ late at night.

6. He was _____ sensitive to pain.

7. The deer ran _____ and _____ through the grass.

8. The truck bounced _____ over the dirt road.

Label each group of words below *nouns, verbs, pronouns, adjectives,* or *adverbs.*

1. slow, ugly, sinful, cute, marvelous, rancid, blue _____

2. Charles, Canada, Kansas, India, Polaroid, Kojak _____

3. poke, plow, speak, throw, penetrate, plunge, sweep _____

4. quietly, awfully, very, terribly, fast, singly, charmingly _____

5. they, our, we, I, you, us, he, she, it, their, ours _____

Underline the adverbs in the following sentences. Some sentences may contain more than one adverb.

1. The car drove quickly through the city.

2. It was cold yesterday.

3. They were terribly afraid of dying.

4. It was an awfully hot day.

5. It was very nice of you to bring me flowers.

6. He walked haltingly along the street toward the car.

7. You could scarcely see the moon for all the clouds.

8. You are trying to do that paper too fast.

9. I told him that I was frankly disgusted by his language.

10. She acted coldly toward him.

11. Please write to me often.

12. The mosquitoes were extremely annoying tonight.

13. She was awfully sorry about the accident.

14. The orchestra played beautifully.

15. It was a truly beautiful day.

16. I think he was really sorry about what he said.

17. Slowly and carefully the doctors began the operation.

18. His heart was barely beating when they brought him into the hospital.

19. During the summer, she lay lazily in a hammock.

20. There was scarcely enough room for everyone in the car.

Review Test 32

Correct the mistake in each group of words below, and write the problem on the line to the right.

Choose from this list:

sentence fragment

slang

double negative

run-on sentence

needs period

needs question mark

needs exclamation mark

needs capitals

needs quotation marks

needs apostrophe to show possession

needs apostrophe to make a contraction

needs comma

needs colon

needs semicolon

wrong use of *to/two/too*

wrong use of *there/their/they're*

no problem

1. The boys mother was in the hospital. _____

2. Be careful watch out for traffic do well in school. _____

3. She was driving to fast for the road conditions. _____

4. Biting down hard on his finger. _____

5. I'm amazed, she said. I didn't think she could do it. _____

6. That book is for the birds. _____

7. Quick, get out of the way _____

8. You'll need a few things a large box, a map, and a shovel. _____

9. There house caught on fire. _____

10. I wont stand for that. _____

11. I can't seem to be able to get no information about him. _____

12. It's better to be safe than sorry. _____

13. This house was destroyed the one next door was untouched. _____

14. Can you see the ship on the horizon _____

15. He leaned over and said "Will you give me this dance?" _____

16. The whole family went to synagogue on saturday. _____

17. The plane landed safely _____

Circle the suffixes in the following words.

1. operator   2. important   3. barely   4. shouting   5. likeness   6. intentionally

For each word below, circle the prefix, and write the meaning of the whole word on the line to the right.

1. misfire _____   3. unintended _____

2. submarine _____   4. bicycle _____

(continued)

5. inexpensive _____   6. postelection _____

Of the following words, circle the one that has a different consonant sound from the rest of the group.

1. chipmunk   2. cheater   3. chorus   4. chatter   5. chortle

After each word, write the long or short vowel sound that it makes.

1. apple __ 2. dimple __ 3. higher __ 4. hippie __ 5. chop __ 6. moth __ 7. eager __ 8. reed __

Label the following sentence *declarative, interrogative, imperative,* **or** *exclamatory.*

1. I'm not going! _____

Write four common nouns.

1. _____   2. _____   3. _____   4. _____

Use numbers to show the order of the following parts of a friendly letter.

____ Closing   ____ Date   ____ Signature

____ Salutation   ____ Body of Letter   ____ Your Address

Underline a subject once and a predicate twice.

1. The lead horse stumbled and fell, and her brother's second-place horse won.

The words *the, a, an* are called *articles.* Articles go before nouns.

Write *ART* under the articles in the following sentences.

1. The thief broke into the store and stole a color television.
   ART   ART   ART

2. An elephant tusk is made of a substance called ivory.

3. The woman was frightened of the dark.

4. He walked for an hour before he saw a gas station.

5. The table was made out of an expensive wood called mahogany.

Use *a* before nouns beginning with consonants and use *an* before nouns beginning with vowels *a, e, i, o,* and *u.*

Fill in the blanks below with the right articles.

1. _an_ apple
2. _a_ supper
3. ____ elevator
4. ____ test tube
5. ____ animal

6. ____ tree
7. ____ umbrella
8. ____ tennis ball
9. ____ Alka-Seltzer
10. ____ castle

11. ____ elephant
12. ____ yelp
13. ____ underdog
14. ____ brownie
15. ____ itch

16. ____ treat
17. ____ broom
18. ____ dentist
19. ____ sugar bowl
20. ____ idiot

Many prepositions tell where things are or where they went. They are words like *across, along, around, at, by, down, for, from, in, into, of, on, onto, over, through, to, under, with.*

Write *PREP* under the prepositions in the following sentences.

1. The car drove through the red light.
                  PREP

2. She gave the book to her best friend.

3. The cat was hiding under the table.

4. He slid across the floor and jumped onto the couch.

5. The book was by Eldridge Cleaver.

Articles (*the, a, an*) go before nouns.
Many prepositions tell where things are or where they went. They are words like *across, along, around, at, by, down, for, from, in, into, of, on, onto, over, through, to, under, with.*

In the following sentences, put *ART* under the articles and *PREP* under the prepositions. The first sentence has been done for you.

1. The plane fell from the clouds onto the ground.
   ART   PREP ART   PREP ART

2. The man was in the army.

3. A police officer stopped the car on the highway.

4. The man was seven feet tall in his shoes.

5. The water roared over the waterfall into the ravine.

6. Many people think an apple a day is good for you.

7. The kids walked along the trail and into the woods.

8. They crawled along the roof and down the side of the warehouse.

9. A detective solved the case in two days.

10. The car skidded all the way across the road.

Make the following groups of words into sentences by adding articles and prepositions. Do your writing on the lines below each group of words. The first sentence has been done for you.

1. man walked store

   The man walked into the store.

2. lady went doctor

   _____

3. car crashed river and sank bottom

   _____

4. plane flew Chicago and landed airport

   _____

Articles (*the, a, an*) go before nouns.
Many prepositions tell where things are or where they went. They are words like *across, along, around, at, by, down, for, from, in, into, of, on, onto, over, through, to, under, with.*

In the following sentences, put *ART* under the articles and *PREP* under the prepositions. The first sentence has been done for you.

1. The lion pounced on the antelope.
   ART   PREP ART
2. An elephant walked along the river.

3. The doctor walked down the corridor with his patient.

4. The sky was a beautiful pink in the evening.

5. The bullet went right through the car.

6. The diver jumped straight into the water and swam across the pool.

7. The writer dedicated the book to his mother.

8. A submarine was hiding under the surface of the lake.

Make the following groups of words into sentences by adding articles and prepositions. Do your writing on the lines provided.

1. horse fell while it jumped fence

   _____

2. rocket was launched moon

   _____

3. candidate gave speech huge crowd street New York

   _____

Write *nouns, verbs, pronouns, adjectives, adverbs, articles,* or *prepositions* on the lines to the right of each group below.

1. he, she, it, they, me, I, you, theirs _____

2. especially, quickly, slowly, painfully, very _____

3. store, bank, lake, man, Chicago, jet, helicopter _____

4. for, by, around, through, into, under, over, to _____

5. swim, catch, run, steal, break, strangle, go _____

6. a, an, the _____

7. funny, sad, friendly, special, nice, blue _____

Write *ART* under the articles and *PREP* under the prepositions in the following sentences.

1. The boy was swimming across the pool.

2. An alligator bit into her leg.

3. The party lasted way into the night.

4. The natives on the frontier ambushed the caravan.

5. She dove into the icy-cold water and swam to the other side of the pool.

6. The plane flew over the mountains and into the clouds.

Make the following groups of words into sentences by adding articles and prepositions. Write on the lines provided.

1. police cars drove scene crime

_____

2. president made speech television 9:30 P.M.

_____

3. scissors cut paper small pieces

_____

4. snake wrapped itself tree

_____

Write *nouns, verbs, pronouns, adjectives, adverbs, articles,* or *prepositions* on the lines to the right of each group.

1. ring, dance, sing, catch, fall, throw _____

2. a, an, the _____

3. pretty, small, enormous, black, brave, strong _____

4. he, she, it, they, we, us, their _____

5. across, along, at, down, for, from, in, of, on, onto _____

6. wheel, airplane, clouds, buildings, idea, brains _____

7. quickly, slowly, fast, straight, nearly, brazenly _____

Write _ART_ under the articles and _PREP_ under the prepositions in the following sentences.

1. A soldier jumped through the window.

2. The gun shot the man in the leg.

3. The woman walked sadly across the field.

4. The horse jumped swiftly over the fence.

5. An octopus wrapped its tentacles around the leg of the frightened man.

6. He bit into the apple.

7. The wind blew through the open window.

8. A light was burning in the study.

9. He pounded away on the typewriter in the library.

10. The cavalry arrived with help for the soldiers.

Now make the following groups of words into sentences by adding prepositions and articles. Write on the lines provided.

1. he always drank coffee morning

_____

2. train arrived station very late

_____

3. general made soldiers march small village

_____

Correct the mistake in each group of words below, and write the problem on the line to the right.

Choose from this list:

sentence fragment

slang

double negative

run-on sentence

needs period

needs question mark

needs exclamation mark

needs capitals

no problem

needs quotation marks

needs apostrophe to show possession

needs apostrophe to make a contraction

needs comma

needs colon

needs semicolon

wrong use of *to/two/too*

wrong use of *there/their/they're*

1. That was the best restaurant in town _____

2. I'm famished I need a meal let's go eat. _____

3. This is the road follow it for two miles. _____

4. There going to lose that game because of him. _____

5. Get going, for heaven's sake _____

6. Working until the early hours of the morning. _____

7. Mr. President what are you doing about inflation? _____

8. The mail carriers bag ripped open. _____

9. The man didn't think his child was particularly fat. _____

10. Get off my back, Jack. _____

11. He shouted into the microphone, Clear the hall. Open the doors. _____

12. She went right two sleep. _____

13. Lets find out what really happened. _____

14. Where did you say that map was kept _____

15. Buy these things at the store milk, eggs, baloney, and cheese. _____

16. I can't see how none of them made it alive. _____

17. did you say i could leave? _____

Label the following pairs *synonyms, antonyms,* or *homonyms.*

1. gracious/rude _____   2. often/seldom _____

Use diagonal lines to divide the following words into syllables.

1. greatest   2. significant   3. fastening   4. grapevine   5. settler   6. banjo

(continued)

Review Test 33

Use numbers to show alphabetical order.

_____ fixed   _____ figment   _____ fought   _____ famous   _____ fill   _____ fired   _____ figure

Write the plurals of the following nouns.

1. shoe _____   5. tax _____

2. lass _____   6. life _____

3. potato _____   7. party _____

4. match _____   8. jockey _____

Write the past tense of the following verbs.

1. send _____   4. bring _____   7. shoot _____

2. fill _____   5. cry _____   8. fall _____

3. hit _____   6. do _____   9. chop _____

What is the future tense of the following verbs?

1. buy _____   2. cry_____

Supply pronouns for the words which are underlined. Write the pronouns above the underlined words.

1. The man and his dog walked toward the old lady.

2. You and I have known Charles since Charles was five years old.

Conjunctions are words that join parts of sentences. Some conjunctions are *and, but, because, so,* and *or.*

Circle the conjunctions in the following sentences.

1. She walked to the beach and saw her brother.

2. He was fifteen years old, but the man wouldn't let him drive the car.

3. She walked all the way home because she forgot the list.

4. The principal got mad and suspended Jimmy and his friends.

5. George and Johnny finished their work and had lots of time to relax.

6. It was raining, so they had to postpone the trip.

7. Either come here or call me on the telephone.

8. She practiced for a long time, and she learned how to type without looking.

9. She ran as fast as she could, but she still lost the race.

10. It was a very sad day, so they decided not to visit anyone.

Interjections are short exclamations followed by an exclamation mark. *Oh!* and *Good grief!* are interjections.

Circle the interjections in the following sentences.

1. Oh no! She is drowning.

2. Here comes the monster. Help!

3. Good heavens! He's the winner.

4. Oh my! I think I'm going to faint.

5. I can't believe it's true. No!

6. Look out! That car is about to explode.

7. Yes! That's the answer I've been looking for.

8. He missed the touchdown by two feet. Darn!

9. Man! You should have seen the size of the sandwich he ate.

10. Fool! Can't you be more careful?

Put *CON* under the conjunction and *INT* under the interjection.

1. Good grief! You are always playing and never serious.

Conjunctions and Interjections 2

Remember:
> *Conjunctions* join parts of sentences; *and, but, because, so, or* are conjunctions.
> *Interjections* are short exclamations; *Oh no!* and *Heavens!* are interjections.

In the following sentences, write *CON* under the conjunctions and *INT* under the interjections.

1. The car came around the corner and entered the finishing stretch.

2. Darn! I don't see anything out there.

3. They said they were coming, but I don't think they will now.

4. Shoot! Either say something or sit down.

5. She bought the cake so you could eat it.

6. Look out! That man is crazy and might do anything.

7. Our horse came in second or third. Great!

8. The plant grew and grew and grew until it was ten feet tall.

9. Fool! How could you have been so stupid and forgotten the money?

10. No! It can't be true; you must be lying.

Label each group of words *nouns, verbs, pronouns, adjectives, adverbs, articles, prepositions, conjunctions,* or *interjections.*

1. through, by, for, around, under _____

2. jump, fly, sing, dance _____

3. and, but, because, so, or _____

4. he, she, it, they, we _____

5. automobile, skyscraper, bath _____

6. a, an, the _____

7. pretty, nice, bright, quick _____

8. Oh! No! _____

9. slowly, painfully, quickly _____

Conjunctions and Interjections 3

Write *CON* under the conjunctions and *INT* under the interjections.

1. She took a nap and woke up at four-thirty.

2. Wow! What a wonderful meal.

3. Good heavens! I can't stand the pain, and I think I'm going to cry.

4. Jump! The train is going to explode.

5. They didn't hear you because the car was making so much noise.

6. The outfielder threw the ball, and the coach yelled, "Slide!"

In the following sentences, put in conjunctions that sound right.

1. They went to the theater, _____ it was closed.

2. He hit her _____ she was saying nasty things about his mother.

3. They were feeling happy, _____ they went for a walk.

4. The car broke down, _____ they had to walk ten miles.

Write in your own interjections on the lines below. Don't forget to put the right punctuation after each interjection.

1. _____ I can't find my pencil.

2. The plane is going to crash. _____

3. _____ I can't put up with this any more.

4. _____ The enemy is attacking.

Label each group *nouns, verbs, pronouns, adjectives, adverbs, articles, prepositions, conjunctions,* or *interjections*.

1. and, but, because _____

2. she, he, it _____

3. Oh no! Help! _____

4. for, by, through _____

5. a, an, the _____

6. woman, Cadillac, bear _____

7. sunny, freezing, open _____

8. kill, lift, sing _____

9. painfully, straight, slowly _____

Write _CON_ under the conjunctions and _INT_ under the interjections in the following sentences.

1. Golly! What a beautiful woman.

2. Oh no! I think she is going to hit me.

3. Jump! That car is out of control.

4. She went to the beach and got a suntan.

5. Darn! I lost my new pen.

6. Gadzooks! It's the incredible shrinking monster.

7. There's no gasoline, so we'd better stay home.

8. There! Take that, you swine.

9. As the dog bit him, he said, "Ouch!"

10. You and your sister are driving me crazy.

11. They went to the drive-in, but it was full when they arrived.

12. Let's watch that program and see what it's about.

Label each group of words _nouns, verbs, pronouns, adjectives, adverbs, articles, prepositions, conjunctions,_ or _interjections._

1. a, an, the _____

2. Nuts! Darn! _____

3. shoot, throw _____

4. and, but _____

5. pretty, small _____

6. he, they, we _____

7. hockey, singer, bus _____

8. awfully, very _____

9. to, by, around _____

Write *CON* under the conjunctions and *INT* under the interjections in the following sentences.

1. Goodness! What is going on here?

2. Come on! Stop playing around and start the game.

3. She went home and cried all night.

4. Good heavens! He is going to win the race and keep the trophy.

5. Fool! Why don't you shut up?

6. Holy mackerel! I've lost my hat.

7. They tried everything, but they didn't try torture.

8. The typewriters were broken, so no one could use them.

9. Gee! I've never seen a woman that beautiful before.

10. Run! That man is after you.

11. The girl failed the test, and all she could say was, "Shoot!"

12. Darn! I blew it again.

13. As the car drove across the street, she shouted, "Wow!"

14. Golly! It's Friday already, and Monday seems like yesterday.

15. The reporter arrived at the scene of the accident, but everyone had left.

Correct the mistake in each group of words below, and write the problem on the line to the right.

Choose from this list:

sentence fragment
slang
double negative
run-on sentence
needs period
needs question mark
needs exclamation mark
needs capitals
no problem

needs quotation marks
needs apostrophe to show possession
needs apostrophe to make a contraction
needs comma
needs colon
needs semicolon
wrong use of *to/two/too*
wrong use of *there/their/they're*

1. Is this your final offer _____

2. Buying everything in sight. _____

3. He lived to be over a hundred years old. _____

4. Some people spend all their money others put some in the bank. _____

5. Send for an ambulance _____

6. You just ain't got the gift of the gab. _____

7. Her uncle gave her fifteen dollars for her birthday _____

8. She didnt think the earth was really round. _____

9. It was there turn to wash the dishes. _____

10. Now Stanley let's have a serious talk. _____

11. Millions of christians gathered to hear the pope speak. _____

12. I don't want to see nothing wrong on this exam. _____

13. Her fathers friends stayed up late playing poker. _____

14. It's early let me sleep some more wake me in an hour. _____

15. I hear what you're saying, said the policeman. I agree. _____

16. It's much to late to change the plans now. _____

17. There were four volunteers Tracy, Kim, Pete, and Sally. _____

Underline a subject once and a predicate twice.

1. The huge bell in the church tower struck noon, and students poured out of class.

What is the fifth part of a business letter? _____

Capitalize the following proper nouns.

1. hitler   2. sentry   3. baseball   4. lake erie   5. mount everest   6. tie

(continued)

Review Test 34

Label the following sentence *declarative, interrogative, imperative,* or *exclamatory*.

1. This game will end in an hour. _____

After each word, write the long or short vowel sound that it makes.

1. sense __ 2. glow __ 3. got __ 4. wire __ 5. mean __ 6. mental __ 7. imply __ 8. grin __ 9. fright __

In each word below, circle the prefix, and write the full meaning of the word on the line to the right.

1. unimportant _____   4. indestructible _____

2. replay _____   5. misconduct _____

3. circumnavigate _____   6. substandard _____

Write the root word on each line.

1. terribly _____   4. sensibly _____

2. courageously _____   5. operational _____

3. fearfully _____

Circle the word which has a different consonant sound from the rest of the group.

1. simple   2. sure   3. sugar   4. ship   5. shopper

Make up your own sentences to fit the pattern of the sample sentence in each block. Make sure you use the part of speech called for at the top of each column.

	article	adjective	noun	verb	adverb
	The	old	man	walked	slowly.
1.					
2.					
3.					

	pronoun	verb	article	adjective	noun
	He	sang	a	beautiful	song.
1.					
2.					
3.					

	article	adjective	noun	verb	pronoun	noun
	The	young	boy	kissed	his	mother.
1.						
2.						
3.						

	pronoun	verb	article	adverb	adjective	noun
	It	was	a	very	beautiful	day.
1.						
2.						
3.						

	article	noun	verb	article	noun
	An	apple	is	a	fruit.
1.					
2.					

Make up your own sentences to fit the pattern of the sample sentence in each block. Make sure you use the part of speech called for at the top of each column.

article	adjective	noun	verb	preposition	article	noun
The	blue	plane	flew	through	the	clouds.
1.						
2.						
3.						

interjection	pronoun	noun	verb	preposition	article	noun
Golly!	Her	uncle	fell	down	the	stairs.
1.						
2.						
3.						

pronoun	verb	adverb	conjunction	adverb
They	walked	slowly	and	carefully.
1.				
2.				
3.				

pronoun	verb	article	adjective	noun
It	was	a	beautiful	meal.
1.				
2.				
3.				

Make up your own interesting sentences to fit the patterns of the sample sentences.

article	noun	verb	adverb	conjunction	adverb	preposition	article	noun
A	car	drove	slowly	and	carefully	under	the	bridge.
1.								
2.								
3.								

article	adjective	adjective	noun	verb	preposition	article	noun
The	tired	old	horse	fell	to	the	ground.
1.							
2.							
3.							

article	noun	verb	adverb	conjunction	adverb
The	boy	worked	quickly	but	carefully.
1.					
2.					
3.					

interjection	pronoun	verb	adjective	noun
Heavens!	I	hate	foolish	people.
1.				
2.				

pronoun	noun	verb	adjective	conjunction	adjective
Their	house	was	small	and	cramped.
1.					
2.					
3.					

Make up your own interesting sentences to fit the pattern of the sample sentences.

	pronoun	verb	adverb	preposition	article	noun
	She	shouted	loudly	at	the	man.
1.						
2.						
3.						

	article	noun	verb	adverb	interjection
	The	train	is coming	quickly.	Look out!
1.					
2.					
3.					

Now try to name the parts of speech in the following sentences. At the top of each column of words, write *noun, verb, adjective, adverb, pronoun, article, conjunction, preposition,* or *interjection.*

1.

That	plane	is	really	fast	and	efficient.
Small	cars	are	very	efficient	but	uncomfortable.

2.

The	old	grey	house	burned	to	the	ground.
An	eager	young	boy	ran	into	the	blaze.

3.

Gracious!	I	thought	you	were	dead.
Good heavens!	We	wished	he	was	handsome.

Write your own good sentences to fit the patterns of the sample sentences.

article	adjective	noun	verb	preposition	article	noun
The	old	church	burned	to	the	ground.
1.						
2.						

pronoun	verb	adjective	conjunction	adjective
He	was	tired	and	sick.
1.				
2.				

pronoun	noun	verb	preposition	pronoun	noun
Her	mother	came	to	her	wedding.
1.					
2.					

pronoun	verb	adverb	conjunction	adverb	preposition	noun
He	walked	sadly	but	quickly	toward	home.
1.						
2.						

interjection	article	adjective	noun	verb
Great Scot!	The	purple	monster	is coming.
1.				
2.				

Correct the mistake in each group of words below, and write the problem on the line to the right.

Choose from this list:

sentence fragment
slang
double negative
run-on sentence
needs period
needs question mark
needs exclamation mark
needs capitals

needs quotation marks
needs apostrophe to show possession
needs apostrophe to make a contraction
needs comma
needs colon
needs semicolon
wrong use of *to/two/too*
wrong use of *there/their/they're*
no problem

1. The food on the plane made some of the people sick. _____

2. Can I help you? asked the policeman. _____

   No, thanks, said the man. _____

3. The banjo. A very popular instrument. _____

4. Will the days get longer in the summer _____

5. Some people like to smoke others hate the smell of cigarettes. _____

6. Didnt I see you downtown the other day? _____

7. Their isn't enough gasoline to get us home. _____

8. Boy oh boy, am I ever ticked off at you. _____

9. The Christmas tree was beautifully decorated _____

10. The grass was getting very long so they decided to cut it. _____

11. Help me I can't do this problem it's too hard. _____

12. I want only two things peace and quiet. _____

13. They drove to new hampshire for thanksgiving. _____

14. He didn't want neither one of them on the team. _____

15. Get the fire extinguisher _____

16. The two girls mothers wouldn't allow them to go out on dates. _____

17. There is just to much too do. _____

Use numbers to show alphabetical order.

_____ Chicago _____ Cincinnati _____ Cleveland _____ Caracas _____ Capetown _____ Custer

Use diagonal lines to break the following words into syllables.

1. dignified 2. nettled 3. caller 4. disgusting 5. selection 6. whiplash

(continued)

Review Test 35

Label the following pairs _synonyms, antonyms,_ or _homonyms._

1. heave/throw _____

2. paste/glue _____

In the following group, circle the word that does not rhyme with the rest.

1. dread   2. dead   3. sled   4. thread   5. red   6. plead   7. bread

Write the plurals of the following nouns.

1. slipper _____

2. foot _____

3. latch _____

4. ax _____

5. valley _____

6. deer _____

7. roof _____

8. Negro _____

9. knife _____

10. country _____

Write the past tense of the following verbs.

1. hate _____

2. grow _____

3. drive _____

4. fall _____

5. dry _____

6. fly _____

7. give _____

8. bounce _____

9. pick _____

10. hear _____

11. cut _____

12. make _____

13. break _____

14. ring _____

Identify the parts of speech in the groups below. Choose from the words in the columns below.

nouns	adverbs	prepositions
verbs	pronouns	conjunctions
adjectives	articles	interjections

1. he, she, him, hers, ours, I, mine _____

2. carefully, slowly, today, fast, directly _____

3. shoot, swing, run, crawl, go, is, was, are, am _____

4. and, but, because, so, or _____

5. nasty, ugly, mean, beautiful, quiet _____

6. a, an, the _____

7. to, by, for, into, over, through, at _____

8. bee, sugar, honey, light, tree _____

9. Gosh! Heavens! Oh! Darn! _____

Name the parts of speech in each sentence. Use the lines below the words to do this. The first sentence has been done for you.

1.

The	hairy	gorilla	grabbed	the	lovely	woman.
article	adjective	noun	verb	article	adjective	noun

2.

He	was	sad	and	walked	home.

3.

Gosh!	You	killed	the	giant	cockroach.

4.

The	woman	drove	very	carefully	on	the	ice.

5.

The	pregnant	woman	was rushed	to	the	hospital.

All Parts of Speech 2

Identify the parts of speech in the groups below. Choose from the words in the columns below.

nouns   adverbs   prepositions
verbs   pronouns   conjunctions
adjectives   articles   interjections

1. cruel, dirty, swift _____

2. Wow! No! Shoot! _____

3. a, an, the _____

4. typewriter, song, dream _____

5. onto, with, under, across _____

6. we, ours, his _____

7. slowly, dutifully, very _____

8. go, shake, cut _____

9. and, but, because _____

Identify the parts of speech in each sentence. Use the lines below the words to do this. The first sentence has been done for you.

1.	Her	best	friend	left	for	a	long	trip.
	pronoun	adjective	noun	verb	preposition	article	adjective	noun

2.	The	doctor	was	very	patient	and	nice.

3.	Good grief!	A	Kung-fu	chop	killed	him.

4.	Softly	and	gently	he	rocked	the	baby.

5.	She	walked	through	the	park	and	collapsed.

Identify the parts of speech in the groups below. Choose from the words in the columns below.

nouns	adverbs	prepositions
verbs	pronouns	conjunctions
adjectives	articles	interjections

1. tickle, squeeze _____

2. on, for _____

3. and, or _____

4. beach, cloud _____

5. the, a _____

6. Doggone! Rats! _____

7. quick, loud _____

8. nicely, loudly _____

9. they, she _____

Name the parts of speech in each sentence. Use the lines below the words to do this.

1.

Her	new	game	broke	on	the	first	day.

2.

The	park	was	quiet	and	peaceful	at	night.

3.

He	parked	the	car	in	a	hugh	garage.

4.

That	man	is	crazy,	stupid,	and	ignorant.

5.

Heavens!	I	forgot	my	wallet	in	the	theater.

Identify the parts of speech in the following sentences. Use the lines below the words to do this.

Parts of speech:

noun	adverb	preposition
verb	pronoun	conjunction
adjective	article	interjection

1.

The	bird	flew	around	the	red	barn.

2.

Chicago	is	often	called	the	windy	city.

3.

She	talked	quietly,	and	people	complained	bitterly.

4.

Gadzooks!	Her	father	will kill	them	because	they	broke

the	big	window	with	the	baseball.

5.

The	new	movie	was	very	exciting	to	the	children.

6.

The	grey	rabbit	ran	under	the	fence,	through

the	barn,	and	into	its	hole.

Test 36 — All Parts of Speech

Identify the parts of speech in the following sentences. Use the lines below the words to do this.

Parts of Speech:

noun	adverb	preposition
verb	pronoun	conjunction
adjective	article	interjection

1.

The	bridge	collapsed	in	the	wild	wind.

2.

He	had	a	terrible	nightmare	about	snakes.

3.

The	cat	crept	slowly	and	silently

toward	the	little	bird.

4.

Shucks!	I	lost	my	favorite	comic.

5.

The	girl	was	intelligent,	attractive,	and	rich.

6.

He	was	handsome	but	very	shy.

7.

Their	team	lost	the	final	game.	Rats!

Final Review Test

Correct the mistake in each group of words below, and write the problem on the line to the right.
Choose from this list:

sentence fragment	needs quotation marks
slang	needs apostrophe to show possession
double negative	needs apostrophe to make a contraction
run-on sentence	needs comma
needs period	needs colon
needs question mark	needs semicolon
needs exclamation mark	wrong use of *to/two/too*
needs capitals	wrong use of *there/their/they're*
	no problem

1. I guess I wasn't thinking when I did that. _____

2. There not going to send us any presents. _____

3. He paced up and down the room and finally he reached for the phone. _____

4. Bitterly complaining for hours and hours. _____

5. Get out, get out, there's a bomb _____

6. Bad news travels fast. _____

7. The period ended the students got up and left the teacher wept. _____

8. She asked whether she could come too _____

9. This is not good enough, said the nurse. I need more information. _____

10. The to of you will need to see me tomorrow. _____

11. She couldn't find her slippers nowhere in the house. _____

12. You burn me up! _____

13. if you don't listen, you'll never find the house. _____

14. Did she say what her name was _____

15. I'm tired let's have the meeting tomorrow. _____

16. Dannys bicycle was stolen from the boys clubhouse. _____

17. You have math on these days Tuesday, Thursday, and Friday. _____

Underline a subject once and a predicate twice.

1. The weather in that part of the country was bad, and they postponed their trip.

Use numbers to show the correct order of the parts of a business letter.

____ Date   ____ Closing   ____ Your Address   ____ Signature

____ Salutation   ____ Body of Letter   ____ Name and Address of Addressee

(continued)

What do you do to the first word in every paragraph?_____

Which of the parts of a business letter does a friendly letter not have?_____

Capitalize the proper nouns.

1. leather   2. new mexico   3. city   4. george   5. jew   6. light

After each sentence, add the correct punctuation, and write *declarative, interrogative, imperative,* or *exclamatory*.

1. How can you say that__ _____   3. The blister healed__ _____

2. Such terrible language__ _____   4. Send that letter now__ _____

After each word, write the long or short vowel sound that it makes.

1. catch __   2. fight __   3. Dane __   4. mighty __   5. pen __   6. slider __   7. pill __

Of the following words, circle the one that has a different consonant sound at the end from the rest in the group.

1. lose   2. loose   3. nose   4. hose   5. sneeze   6. grows

For each word below, circle the prefix, and write the full meaning of the word on the line to the right.

1. submarine _____   3. antislavery _____

2. mislead _____   4. unnerving _____

In the words below, circle the suffixes, and write the root words on the lines to the right.

1. gracefully _____   4. terribly _____

2. sincerity _____   5. awfully _____

3. agreement _____   6. famous _____

Use numbers to show alphabetical order.

____ machine   ____ match   ____ marvel   ____ melting   ____ march   ____ mile

Use diagonal lines to divide the following words into syllables.

1. lasso   2. instrument   3. framework   4. mustache   5. publication

Label the following pairs *synonyms, antonyms,* or *homonyms*.

1. irate/angry_____   3. attractive/repulsive _____

2. great/grate _____

(continued)

139

In the following group, circle the word that doesn't rhyme with the others.

1. freak   2. leak   3. break   4. teak   5. meek   6. beak

Write the plurals of the following nouns.

1. house _____   4. tomato _____   7. dish _____

2. tax _____   5. half _____   8. man _____

3. country _____   6. jockey _____   9. deer _____

Write the past tense of the following verbs.

1. bite _____   6. fight _____

2. talk _____   7. catch _____

3. dance _____   8. run _____

4. cry _____   9. is _____

5. chop _____   10. know _____

Write the future tense of the following verbs.

1. I talk _____   2. She sits _____

Above the underlined words, write pronouns which could be used to replace the words.

1. That dog was Karen's, but Bill and Andy stole that dog.

Identify the parts of speech in the groups below. Choose from the following words.

nouns	adverbs	prepositions
verbs	pronouns	conjunctions
adjectives	articles	interjections

1. and, but, because _____

2. saddle, dream, life _____

3. he, I, ours _____

4. by, for, around _____

5. seek, throw, settle _____

6. a, an, the _____

7. simple, high, tiny _____

8. Heavens! Good grief! _____

9. painfully, very, awfully _____